lsr - 1924

NL checklists

Humor of Some Fantasy

"Glimpses of the Future"
ghosts - "Letter to Spiritualist"

etc.

THE GARDEN
OF FOLLY

THE GARDEN OF FOLLY

BY STEPHEN LEACOCK

"This poor old world works hard and gets
no richer: thinks hard and gets no wiser:
worries much and gets no happier. It casts off
old errors to take on new ones: laughs at
ancient superstitions and shivers over modern
ones. It is at best but a Garden of Folly,
whose chattering gardeners move a moment
among the flowers, waiting for the sunset."

(*Confucius—or Tutankhamen—I forget which*)

NEW YORK
DODD, MEAD AND COMPANY
1924

PRINTED IN U. S. A.

VAIL-BALLOU PRESS, INC.
BINGHAMTON AND NEW YORK

PREFACE

CONCERNING HUMOUR AND HUMOURISTS

I do not claim that this preface has anything in particular to do with the book that follows. Readers who desire to do so, and are mean enough, may safely omit either the book or the preface without serious loss. I admit that the preface is merely inserted in order to give me a chance to expound certain views on the general nature of humour and on the general aspects of the person called the humourist.

There is a popular impression that a humourist or comedian must needs be sad; that in appearance he should be tall, lantern-jawed and cadaverous; and that his countenance should wear a woe-begone expression calculated to excite laughter. The loss of his hair is supposed to increase his market value, and if he is as

v

bald as a boiled egg with the shell off, his reputation is assured.

This I think springs from the fact that, in the past at least, people did not propose to laugh with *the humourist but* at *him. They laughed in an apologetic way. They considered him simply* too *silly. He wrung a laugh from them in spite of their better selves.*

In other words, till our own time laughter was low. Our dull forefathers had no notion of its intellectual meaning and reach. The Court jester, referred to haughtily as "yon poor fool," was most likely the cleverest man around the Court; and yet historical novels are filled with little touches such as this;—

"The King sank wearily upon his couch. 'My Lady,' he said, 'I am aweary. My mind is distraught. In faith I am like to become as deftless as yon poor fool.'"

Now as a matter of fact, the King was probably what we should call in North America a "great big boob"; and the poor fool if he had lived with us would be either on the staff of LIFE *or* PUNCH, *or at the head*

vi

of a University—whichever he pleased.

A generation or so ago the idea of the melancholy humourist got a lot of corroboration from the fact that some of the best humourists of the time were in actual reality of a woe-begone appearance. The famous Bill Nye was tall, mournful, and exceedingly thin, a fact which he exploited to the full. He used to tell his hearers that there had been a request for him to come to them again and to appear "in broadsword combat with a parallel of latitude." The still more celebrated Artemus Ward was also of a shambling and woe-begone habit; his melancholy face and feeble frame bespoke in reality the ravages of a mortal disease. The laughter that greeted his shambling appearance and his timid gestures appear in retrospect as cruel mockery. The humour of Ward's public appearance which captivated the London of sixty years ago is turned now to pathos.

But Ward and Nye are only two examples of the "melancholy comedian," a thing familiar through the ages. Yet in spite of all such pre-

cedents, and admitting that exceptions are exceptions, I cannot but think that the true manner of the comedian is that of smiles and laughter. If I am to be amused let me see on the stage before me, not the lantern jaws of sorrow but a genial countenance shaped like the map of the world, lit with spectacles, and illuminated with a smile. Let me hear the comedian's own laughter come first and mine shall follow readily enough, laughing not at him, but with him. I admit that when the comedian adopts this mode he runs the terrible risk of being the only one to laugh at his own fun. This is indeed dreadful. There is no contempt so bitter as that of the man who will not laugh for the man who will. The poor comedian's merriment withers under it and his laughter turns to a sad and forced contortion pitiful to witness. But it is a risk that he must run. And there is no doubt that if he can really and truly laugh his audience will laugh with him. His only difficulty is in doing it.

This much however, I will admit, that if a man has a genuine sense of humour, he is apt to take a somewhat melancholy, or at least a disillusioned view of life. Humour and disillusionment are twin sisters. Humour cannot exist alongside of eager ambition, brisk success, and absorption in the game of life. Humour comes best to those who are down and out, or who have at least discovered their limitations and their failures. Humour is essentially a comforter, reconciling us to things as they are in contrast to things as they might be.

This is why I think such a great number of people are cut off from having any very highly developed sense of humour.

If I had to make a list of them I would put at the head all eminent and distinguished people whose lofty position compels them to take themselves seriously. The list would run something like this.

1. The Pope of Rome. I doubt if he could have a very keen sense of fun.

2. Archbishops and the more dignified clergy, sense of humour—none.

3. Emperors, Kaisers, Czars, Emirs, Emus, Sheiks, etc, etc,—absolutely none.

4. *Captains of Industry (I mean the class that used to be called "Nation Makers" and are now known as "profiteers")—atrophied.*

5. *Great scholars, thinkers, philanthropists, martyrs, reformers, and patriots,—petrified.*

As against this I would set a list of people who probably would show a sense of humour brought to its full growth;—

1. *Deposed kings.*

2. *Rejected candidates for election to a national legislature.*

3. *Writers whose work has been refused by all the publishers.*

4. *Inventors who have lost their patents, actors who have been hooted off the stage, painters who can't paint, and speaking broadly, all the unemployed and the unsuccessful.*

I have no doubt that this theory, like most of the things that I say in this book, is an overstatement. But I have always found that the only kind of statement worth making is an overstatement. A half truth, like half a brick, is always more forcible as an argument than a whole one. It carries further.

CONTENTS

xi

I
THE SECRETS
OF SUCCESS

I.—The Secrets of Success

*As Revealed at One Dollar and Fifty
Cents a Revelation*

*Note. This opening chapter deals with the
secrets of material success and shows how
easily it can be achieved. Indeed anybody
who is willing to take a brief correspondence
course can achieve it in a few weeks. What
follows here is based upon the best and newest
manuals on the subject, and every word is
guaranteed.*

The New Race of Big Men and Big Women

DEAR friend reader—for you will not mind my calling you this, or both of this, for I feel already that we are friends, are we not, don't you?—let us sit down and have a comfortable get-together visit and talk things over.

3

Are you aware that there is a big movement going on in this country, and that a lot of big-hearted men and ever so many big women are in it? Perhaps not. Then let me try to tell you all about it and the way in which the world is being transformed by it.

No, don't suggest sending me any money. I don't want it. Neither I nor any of these big men and women who are working on this thing want money. We all take coupons, however, and if you care to cut out any coupons from any newspaper or magazine and send them to me I shall be glad to get them. But, remember, *sending a coupon pledges you to nothing*. It does not in any way bring you within reach of the law, and you may cut out as many as you like. Only a little while ago a young boy, scarcely more than a man, came into my office in great distress and in evident remorse. "What have I done?" he moaned. "What is it?" I asked. "I have cut out a coupon," he said, wringing his hands, "and sent it in." "To where?" I asked. "To Department B. The Success Editor, Box 440-J.

4

Phoenix, Arizona." "My dear friend," I said, "cutting out a coupon pledges you to nothing." He left my office (after in vain offering me money) a new being. I may say that he is now at the head of one of the biggest dried-prune businesses in Kalamazoo.

In other words, that boy had found the secret of success. A chance remark had suddenly put him in the path of Opportunity.

My dear reader, you may be, all unknowing, in exactly the position of that young man. You may be, like him, on the very verge of opportunity. Like him, you may need only a friendly shove to put you where you belong.

Now this movement that I am in, along with these big women, etc., that I spoke of, is a movement for putting success within reach of all, even of the dullest. You need not despair merely because you are dull. That's nothing. A lot of these big men in the movement were complete nuts before they came in.

Perhaps it is a new idea to you that success can be deliberately achieved. Let me assure you, on the contrary, that achieving it is the only way to get it.

I wonder, for example, if the thought has ever occurred to you that you would like your salary raised. If so, nothing is more simple. Read the chapters which follow and your salary will be raised before you finish them. After having studied the literature of this big movement for success, I can tell you of hundreds, of thousands, of men and women in this country whose salaries have been raised beyond recognition.

What would you say, for example, to earning sixty-three dollars a week without leaving home, and using only your spare time; and that, too, at an agreeable occupation, needing no preparation and no skill? Do you want to do it? Well, that is what young Edward Bean-head—Kid Ed, they call him—is doing right at this minute in Houston, Texas.

Or what do you say to cleaning up half a million cold in a fortnight, on the sale of an article indispensable to every home in the country, easily understood and never out of order, patent applied for? Well, that was what was done by Callicot Johnson—Cal. Johnson, they generally call him, at least if they're busy, or Millionaire Johnson, or Lucky Johnson—they call him a lot of names like that. You can see his picture in half the papers in the country— Bull Johnson, he's often called—you must have seen him. Well, here was a man, this Cal, or this Bull, who never knew till he was forty-one years old that he had *personality,* and then all of a sudden, one day—but, stop—I'll tell you later on all about this Bull, or Buffalo Johnson. They often call him Buffalo. I merely say that at present Buffalo—or Buff—is at the head of one of the biggest nut syndicates in El Paso.

Or how would you like to imagine yourself becoming the head of one of the biggest mercantile concerns in the country? Would you have any use for it? I mean, would it make a hit with you? If so, I shall have to tell you presently about Robert J. Rubberheart—Bull Dog Bob they usually call him. It occurred to Bob one day that eighty-five per cent of his efficiency was being squandered in—but, no, I'd better keep it. Suffice it to say that you can see, in the back pages of almost any of the current magazines, a picture of Bob at his mahogany desk in his office in that mercantile firm. He is pointing his finger right at his stenographer's eye, and underneath him is written, *"This man earns ten dollars a minute."* Well, that's Bob. He has cut out the waste of his efficiency and he has "made good."

But talking of Bull Dog Bob and the way he "made good," reminds me of a lot of other cases which I have met in my study of this big movement, of men, yes, and of women, who have "made good." Perhaps you don't realize, reader, that no matter if a man is a long way down, almost down and out, he can still "come back" and "make good." If a man has got sufficient pep and grit not to let the sand get choked out of him he will come back every time. I am thinking here specially—as no doubt you are—of the instance of the Hon. E. Final Upshot, now one of the leading men, one of the *big* men in the senate of Nicaragua. Yet *there* was a man who had been nearly beaten out by

8

fate; health gone, friends gone, memory gone
—he couldn't even have remembered his friends
if he had kept them—money gone, everything
in fact, except that somewhere away down in
that man was sand. And so one day just by
chance, Ed—his friends now always called him
Honest Ed—saw in a paper . . . but don't
let's spoil the story.

In any case, the real point is that men like
Buff Johnson, and Bull Dog Bob, and the Honorable Final Upshot have got *personality*.
That's it. Some of them had it from the start
but didn't know it. You may be in that class.
Concealed in these men was an unsuspected as-
set, like the jewel in the toad of which Shakespeare speaks. It may be in you.

And having personality, they set to work
to develop themselves. They built up their
efficiency. They studied their bodies. They
took exercises which gave them constitutions
like ostriches. They eliminated waste. They
chewed their food for hours before they used it.
Realizing that a ferruginous diet breaks down
the tissues and sets up a subterfuge of gas

9

throughout the body, they took care to combine in their diet a proper proportion of explosives. Having grasped the central fact that the glory of a man's strength is in his hair, these people, by adopting a system of rubbing (easily learned in six lessons and involving nothing more than five minutes of almost hysterical fun every morning), succeeded in checking the falling of the follicles, or capillary basis of the hair itself. In short, as one of the greatest of them has said, *"Hair power is brain power."*

As with personality and efficiency, so with memory. These men of the class of which we are speaking, grasped the idea that Memory Means Money. To gain it, they adopted a simple formula (easily learned in six lessons without sending money) first invented by the ancient Aztecs, but now made available for everybody by the splendid efforts of the famous Doctor Allforce. The doctor, whose picture shows him to be a G. D. M. of Kansas, is often called (presumably by his friends) the Wizard of Mind Power. He is a man of whom we shall have a lot to say. Undoubtedly the man has psychic power. Whether or not it is the selfsame psychic power enjoyed by Ancient Chaldeans and the Magi who make the Magi Water, is a point on which we must not try to pronounce. But the man certainly has it, and no doubt it was for that that Kansas gave him his G. D. M. The Doctor claims that memory can be built up by a *rearrangement of the colloid particles of the human brain.* So convinced is the doctor of the validity of this daring claim that he offers a *personal guarantee* of $100 (one hundred dollars) for anybody disproving it to his satisfaction. Thus far, no single professor of any of the colleges (all known to be effete) has come forward to challenge this daring piece of scientific prophylaxis. In short, as the doctor himself says, *Hypothesis is truth!*

But we must not talk of the Doctor too much. We shall have plenty to say of him in his place. Just remember him as the *Man Who Does Not Forget.* We only mention him here in this connection as one of the big men whose ideas are reshaping the globe. Indeed, the Doctor himself has gone on record with the words, *"I can reshape your head."*

But even all that we have said does not exhaust the scope of this great movement which is building up a new race of men and women. There are bigger things yet. Have you ever thought of the large place that *love* plays in this world? Perhaps not. You may be too big a boob to have thought about it. And yet it is a thing about which every well-constituted man and every well-constructed woman ought to think. If you have hitherto been clean outside of our great movement toward the new life and the new success you have probably never read the booklet (obtainable anywhere or to be had by cutting out a coupon) entitled *How to Choose a Mate.* Apart from its obvious usefulness at sea, this is a little book that should be studied by every young man and woman in the land. It is written by a man whose name of course you know, Dr. O. Salubrious, Med. Mis. Wash. He practically gives it away.

It may never have occurred to you how many

men in picking a mate, or a life companion, or even a wife, make a bad pick. There are ever so many cases on record where serious dissatisfaction arises with the selection which has been made. With so many to choose from, this seems unnecessary. If you will study the work of Dr. Salubrious you will see that he makes the bold claim that men and women are animals and they should mate with the same care as is shown by the lobster, the lizard, and the graminiferous mammalia.

But for the moment we need follow the Doctor no farther. The essential idea which arises from what we have said above is that a new race of men and women is emerging under our eyes. These people like Cal. Johnson and Dr. Salubrious and Doctor Allforce and the Honorable Final Upshot are a new set of beings. Alive with personality, using one hundred per cent of their efficiency, covered with glossy hair rich in its natural oil, forgetting nothing, earning sixty-three dollars a week at occupations which fill only their leisure time, these people are rapidly inheriting the earth. As Doctor—himself has put it, *"The future will belong to those who own it."*

Do you want then, reader—and I am asking you for the last time—to be in this movement or out of it? Or no, let me put it in the striking way phrased by Allforce, *"Can you afford to be out of it?"*

A CHAT ON PERSONALITY: WHAT IT IS
AND HOW TO GET IT

Let us therefore proceed to study out this question quietly and systematically, taking nothing for granted. We have said above that personality is the greatest thing in the world. But now let us ask ourselves: *How do we know* that personality is the greatest thing in the world? From what corollaries do we draw this hypothesis, and is such an innuendo justified? In other words, who says so?

Our answer to this is very simple. The greatest men in the world, those, that is to say, who draw the largest salaries, do so by their personality. Ask any truly great man how he made all his money, and he will always tell you the same thing. The bigger the man is the more loudly he will say it.

The other day I had a few minutes' conversation (I couldn't afford more) with one of the biggest-priced men in this country. "To what," I asked, "do you attribute your own greatness?" He answered without hesitation, "To myself."

Yet this was a man who has the reputation of being the second biggest consumer of crude rubber in this country. He may do it and he may not, but he has that reputation. I asked another man, a large consumer of adjustable bicycle parts, how much he thought he owed of his present commanding position to education. He answered emphatically, "Nothing." Something in his tone made me believe him.

Now the common element in all these men is personality. Each one of them has a developed, balanced, nicely adjusted well-hung personality. You feel that as soon as such a man is in your presence; when he enters a room, you are somehow aware that he has come in. When he leaves, you realize that he has gone out.   As soon as he opens his mouth, you know that he is speaking.   When he shuts his mouth, you feel that he has stopped.

Until the recent discoveries of the success movement it was not known that personality could be acquired.   We know now that it can.

For the acquirement of personality, the first thing needed is *to get into harmony with yourself*.   You may think that this is difficult.   But a little practice will soon show you how. Make the effort, so far as you can, to set up a *bilateral harmony between your inner and your outer ego*.   When you get this done start and see what you can do to *extend yourself in all directions*.   This is a little hard at first, but the very difficulty will lend zest to the effort.   As soon as you begin to feel that you are doing it, then try, gently at first, but with increasing emphasis, to *revolve about your own axis*.   When you have got this working nicely, slowly and carefully at first, *lift yourself to a new level of thinking*.   When you have got up there, hold it.

As soon as in this way you have got yourself

sufficiently elongated and extended you will have gained the first step in the development of personality, namely Harmony—in other words, you are completely and absolutely satisfied with yourself. If you were a nut before, you will never know it now.

The next great thing to be acquired is optimism, cheerfulness, the absence of all worry. It is a scientific fact that worry has a physical effect upon the body, clogging up the œsophagus and filling the primary ducts with mud. Cheerfulness, on the other hand, loosens up the whole anatomy by allowing a freer play to the bones. Begin each day with a smile. When you rise in the morning, throw open your window wide and smile out of it. Don't mind whom you hit with it. When you descend to the breakfast table try to smile at your food, or even break into a pleasant laugh at the sight of it. When you start off to your place of business, enter your street car in a bright and pleasant way, paying your fare to the conductor with a winsome willingness. When you go into your office, remove your coat and rubbers with a pretty little touch of bonhommie. Ask the janitor, or the night watchman, how he has slept. Greet your stenographer with a smile. Open your correspondence with another smile, and when you answer it, try to put into what you write just the little touch of friendly cheerfulness that will win your correspondent's heart. It is amazing how a little touch of personal affection will brighten up the dull routine of business correspondence like a grain of gold in the sand.

Don't sign yourself "Yours truly," but in some such way as "Yours for optimism," or "Yours for a hundred per cent cheerfulness." But I will show you what I mean in a more extended way by relating to you the amazing—but well-authenticated—story of the rise and success of Edward Beanhead.

The Remarkable Case of Edward Beanhead
An Amazing Story of Success

In presenting in support of what has been written in the preceding paragraphs the instance of Edward Beanhead, I may say that I have no doubt whatever of the authenticity of the story. It is too well attested to admit of doubt. I have seen this story of the rise of Edward Beanhead (under his own and other names) printed in so many journals that it must be true; the more so as the photograph of Beanhead is reproduced beside the story, and in many cases the editor gives a *personal guarantee* that the story is true. In other cases readers who doubt are invited to cut out a coupon which will bring them a free booklet that will give them a course on Leadership.

Another proof of the truth of the story is that Edward Beanhead's salary is often inserted and printed right across the page. I forget what it is; in fact, it is not always the same, but it fills all the available space.

In many cases Beanhead in his photograph is depicted as actually pointing at his salary with one finger and saying, *"Do you want to earn this?"*

Skeptical readers may suggest that Edward must have owed his start in life to early advantages of birth and wealth: he may have been a prince. This is not so. Beanhead had no birth and no wealth. Accounts differ as to where he was born. Some of the documents, as reproduced in the best advertising pages, represent him as a bright little farm boy from Keokuk, Iowa. It is well known, of course. that most railroad presidents and heads of colleges come from there. Pictures are numerous which show Beanhead barefooted and with a five-cent straw hat, standing in what looks like a trout stream. There is a legend *"From Farm Yard to Manager's Desk."* Another school of writers, however, shows Edward as beginning his career in a great city, running errands—at an admirable speed and labeled *"Earning his first dime."*

All this, however, is a matter of controversy. The only thing of which we can be certain is that Edward Beanhead, as a youth just verging into manhood, was occupying a simple station as some sort of business clerk. Here came the turning point of his life. By a happy accident Edward came across a little booklet entitled *Tutankhamen is a Dead One. What are you?*

Learn personal efficiency in six lessons. Write to the Nut University. Post Office Box 6, Canal Street, Buffalo.

From this time on Beanhead's spare minutes were spent in study. We have in proof of this the familiar illustration in which Edward is seen on a high stool, in his office at lunch hour, eating a bun with one hand and studying a book on personality in the other, while at the side, inserted in a sort of little cloud, one can see Edward's two office companions playing craps with two young negroes. The picture is now rather rare, the little vignette of the crap game having proved rather too attractive for certain minds: in fact some people quite mistook the legend *"Do you want to make money fast?"*

Beanhead took the entire course, occupying five weeks and covering Personality, Magnetism, Efficiency, Dynamic Potency, the Science of Power, and Essentials of Leadership.

By the end of his course Edward had reached certain major conclusions. He now saw that Personality is Power; that Optimism opens Opportunity; and that Magnetism Makes

Money. He also realized that Harmony makes for Happiness, and that Worry would merely carry his waste products into his ducts and unfit him for success.

Armed with these propositions, Edward Beanhead entered his office after his five weeks' course a new man.

Instead of greeting his employer with a cold "Good Morning," as many employees are apt to do, Edward asked his superior how he had slept.

Now notice how the little things count. It so happened that his employer hadn't slept decently for ten years; and yet no employee had ever asked him about it. Naturally he "reacted" at once. Edward reacted back and in a few minutes they were in close confabulation. Beanhead suggested to his employer that perhaps his ducts were clogged with albuminous litter. The senior man gravely answered that in that case he had better raise Edward's salary. Beanhead acquiesced with the sole proviso that in that case he should be allowed to organize his employer's business so as to put it

on a strategic footing. Now observe again
how things count. It so happened that this
man, although carrying on a business which extended over six states and out into the ocean,
had never thought of organizing it; and he
didn't even know what a strategic footing was.
The result was a second increase of salary
within twenty-four hours.

In the weeks that followed Edward Beanhead, now seated in a commodious office with
flat-top desk and a view of the ocean and a
range of mountains, entirely reorganized the
firm's business. His method was simple. The
employees were submitted to a ruthless brain-
test which eliminated most of them. The business itself was then plotted out on a chart so
designed as to show at a glance all the places
where the firm did no business. Banks in
which the firm had no money were marked with
a cross. By these and other devices Edward
rapidly placed the business on a new footing,
stopping all the leaks, focusing it to a point,
driving it deep into the ground, giving it room
to expand, and steering it through the rocks.

23

The situation is perhaps more easily understood by stating that henceforth the motto of the business became *"Service."*

The natural upshot of it was that before long Edward Beanhead's employer summoned him up to his office and informed him that he was getting old (he was seven weeks older than when we began with him), and that he was now prepared to retire to a monastery or to a golf club, and that if Edward wanted the business he could have it.

Hence at the end we see Edward Beanhead sitting beside his desk, half revolved in a revolving chair and with a beautiful stenographer within easy touch. There are two little placards nailed up, one on each side of his head bearing the legends *"Efficiency"* and *"Service."*

And one wonders where are those fellows who were playing craps with the negroes.

The Success of Great Men

It is very difficult to leave this topic of success without saying something about the success of great men; indeed there is no reason why I should. I wonder if it has ever occurred to the reader to ask why there are so few great men and why so few men succeed in lifting themselves above the average level. Perhaps it hasn't. But if he did ask why we cannot all raise ourselves above the average, the answer would be, very simply, that we all can if we try.

This is a thing that we realise at once when we study the careers of great men. But to study them properly we must not turn to the dull pages of the college histories. There only a very limited and partial account of the great is found. To get the real facts we must open the advertising pages of the illustrated magazines, and we can see at a glance that they tell us vital things never touched upon by the standard histories.

For example, it is very doubtful whether Bancroft ever knew that George Washington was in the habit of taking four deep breaths just before eating. If he did he never mentions it. Nor does he make any reference to the fact that Benjamin Franklin once said that no perfect breakfast food had as yet been found (that, of course was in his day: it has been found since, as we shall see).

In the same way Lord Macaulay, a man otherwise well informed, does not seem to know that Oliver Cromwell once said "The Secret of making money lies in Scientific Investment." Nor was Shakespeare aware that the cloak or mantle which Julius Caesar wore on the day he overcame the Nervii and which he wore when he was stabbed by his assassins was undoubtedly made by the famous Knit-Knot process, now so widely known.

One asks in vain, what kind of suspenders did Henry of Navarre use? What was it that Charlemagne used to say about carrying a camera with you during a vacation in the Adirondacks? What sort of exercise did Queen Elizabeth take for ten minutes every morning? In what attitude was Lord Bacon standing when he said "Mr. Business Man, why not use a fountain pen?"

But in recent times all these fascinating things are being solved for us by the painstaking researches of the advertising experts. We are getting to know things about our great men that we never knew before,—intimate, personal things that we never knew before.

And of all the historical characters whose careers are being thus illuminated there is one who stands out conspicuously above all others, —The Emperor Napoleon. This great man enjoys, in the success movement, an eminence over all others. It is the aim of everybody to be a Napoleon in his own particular line of activity and a great many are succeeding. You can see their pictures any day.

There are at least thirty-seven Napoleons now doing business. There is a "Napoleon of Billiards" and . . . a "Napoleon of Water Polo," and a "Napoleon of the Rubber Shoe Industry"; and there is also a man who is the "Napoleon of Pants Designers," and another who is the "Napoleon of the Ladies Shirtwaist Business"; there is a dog who is the Napoleon of Airedale Terriers, and there is a cow who is the Napoleon of Holstein milk-givers.

In short it is becoming a very important thing to learn how to be a Napoleon. You have only to turn over the back pages of any of our greatest journals, the serious pages where they teach people how to live and how to sell things,—to see little pictures of Napoleon inserted everywhere. Sometimes there is just his head under his hat: sometimes a full length picture to show his hands clasped behind his back. And in each case there is some little motto that Napoleon said or some statement about his habits. From across the years and over the wastes of the South Atlantic Napoleon is still teaching us how to live and how to sell things.

From these statements thus printed I have pieced together a composite picture of Napoleon in which is shown those little personal things that made him what he was.

Anybody who wants to be a Napoleon has only to imitate these things. I admit that they are a little complicated. But even Napoleon couldn't have learned them all at once. He must have picked them bit by bit.

In the first place the great Emperor was an early riser. The hour of three in the morning saw him in the saddle or at his desk. "Early rising," he once said when taking a well known breakfast food, "not only peptonizes the stomach but with the aid of a simple remedy obtainable at all drug stores restores tone and vigor to the lost digestion."

Napoleon also sat up late. He never sought his couch till three in the morning. "The later the hour," he once said, in referring to a new patent oil lamp, "the better the brain."

It was the practice of Napoleon to chew his food twenty minutes before swallowing it. Eating a sirloin steak took him all day. Napoleon was in the habit of eating standing up. He also ate lying down. He could even sit and eat.

While talking the great Emperor habitually held his mouth firmly shut.

Napoleon always wore wool next to his skin. He once said in an interview which he seems to have given to a well known firm of woollen manufacturers in Paterson, New Jersey, "There is nothing like wool."

In the same way he always said, "There is

nothing like a delicious cup of Ozo when exhausted from the pulpit and the platform."

Napoleon was passionately fond of walking: also he never walked. Napoleon drank, but always with the strictest avidity.

Napoleon made little use of tobacco except in the form of snuff, or cigars or cut plug.

During his exile at St. Helena Napoleon is reported to have said,

"If I had taken a course in Personal Leadership, I should not have landed here."

II

THE HUMAN MIND
UP TO DATE

II.—The Human Mind
Up To Date

Note. The discussion which follows below is intended to be merely a portion, or half portion, of a Manual of the New Mentality. The work when finished will comprise twenty instalments which may be read either singly or all at the same time. The final edition will be bound in half-calf for ordinary readers, with a university edition for scholars (complete calf), and for the rich an édition de luxe *sold at an addition* de luxe.

The object of the entire work—I need hardly say—will not be to make money, but to perform a service to the community. To make this certain, the word service *will be stamped in gilt letters on each volume of a special or "service edition" of the book—sold to servants.*

The Mind Wave

O NE of the most cheering things about this good, gay world in which we are at present living is the recent pleasing progress of the human mind. For ever so many centuries the human mind had lain more or less dormant. It was known that it was there. But just where it was and what it did and how it did it was a matter on which nothing, if anything, was known.

Within recent years all this has changed. A great wave of mind culture has swept over the community. People who never had any before now have little else.

It is generally admitted that the human mind was first discovered about four years ago by a brilliant writer in one of the Sunday journals. His article *"Have We a Subconscious Ego?"* was immediately followed by a striking discussion under the title *"Are We Top Side Up?"* This brought forth a whole series of popular articles and books under such titles as *Willing and Being, How to Think, Existence as a Mode*

34

of Thought, The Super Self, and such special technical studies as *The Mentality of the Hen* and the *Thought Process of the Potato.*

This movement, once started, has spread in every direction. All our best magazines are now full of mind. In every direction one sees references to psychoanalysis, auto-suggestion, hypnosis, hypnoosis, psychiatry, inebriety, and things never thought of a little while ago. Will power is being openly sold by correspondence at about fifty cents a kilowatt. College professors of psychology are wearing overcoats lined with fur, and riding in little coupé cars like doctors. The poor are studying the psychology of wealth, and the rich are studying the psychology of poverty. Memory has been reduced to a system. A good memory is now sold for fifty cents.

Everybody's mind is now analyzed. People who used to be content with the humblest of plain thinking, or with none at all, now resolve themselves into "reflexes" and "complexes" and "impulses." Some of our brightest people are kleptomaniacs, paranoiacs, agoraphobists, and dolomites.   A lot of our best friends turn out to be subnormal and not worth knowing.   Some of the biggest business men have failed in the intelligence test and have been ruined.   A lot of our criminals turn out not to be criminals at all, but merely to have a reaction for another person's money.

Still more gratifying is the fact that we are now able to locate with something like certainty where the mind is.   And it appears that it is away down—in fact, is sinking into a bottomless abyss.   What we took for the mind is only an insignificant part of it, a poor glimmer of intelligence, a rush light floating on the surface of an unknown depth.   Underneath the mind lurks the *subconscious,* and away down under this again, the *subliminal,* and under that is the *primitive complex,* and farther down, fifty feet in the mud, is the *cosmic intelligence.*   This late item, cosmic intelligence, is thought by some people to be found in Buddhism, and other people say that it is seen in Walt Whitman, and in Dante at his best.   It may also be connected with music.

36

But what is now an assured fact is that, while human beings have only just begun to learn about these things, the animals have known about them and been using them for years. It seems that the caterpillar doesn't think at all! He gave it up long ago; he merely "reacts." The common ant *(formica americana)* instead of working all the time, as we thought it did, does not work at all. It merely has a community complex in the lobes of one of its feet. What we took to be the play of the young lamb *(lambens piccola)* is simply a chemical movement of its tail under the influence of one or more stimuli.

In short, the whole mental world has been thrown into the greatest excitement. Everybody is "reacting" on everybody else. Mind waves and brain storms blow about like sand in the Sahara. Things good and bad come at us like an infection. We live in deadly fear that we may catch bolshevism, as we might a cold. Everything rushes at us in "waves." A New York chauffeur chokes his employer, and it is called a "crime wave." The man is rushed off to a rest house to have his complex removed, while the people leave the city in the flood. Then they hear that a repentant burglar has given a million dollars to Trinity Church, and that a moral wave is flooding over the city; and they come back.

In this disturbed state nobody's mind can act alone. Everybody has to be in it with a lot of others. Family love is replaced by Big Brother Movements and Little Sister Agitations, and a grown-up man subscribes twenty-five cents and wears a pink ribbon to help him to be kind to his own mother.

The Outbreak of Psychology

Prominent among all these phenomena is the great movement which is putting psychology into the front rank of human activities. In earlier days this science was kept strictly confined to the colleges. It was taught by an ancient professor in a skull cap, with a white beard which reached to the foot of his waistcoat. It had no particular connection with anything at all, and did no visible harm to those who studied it. It explained the difference between a "sensation" and a "perception" and between an "idea" and a "notion." As a college subject, it was principally taken as a qualification for the football team, and thus ranked side by side with architecture, religious knowledge and the Portuguese Ballad. Some of the greatest players on the Harvard and Yale teams knew little else.

All this changed. As a part of the new research, it is found that psychology can be used not only for the purpose of football, but for almost anything in life. There is now not only psychology in the academic or college sense, but also a Psychology of Business, a Psychology of Education, a Psychology of Salesmanship, a Psychology of Religion, a Psychology of Boxing, a Psychology of Investment, and a Psychology of Playing the Banjo. In sort, everybody has his. There is the psychology of the criminal, the psychology of the politician, and a psychology of the infant. For almost every juncture of life we now call in the services of an expert psychologist as naturally as we send for an emergency plumber. In all our great cities there are already, or soon will be, signs that read "Psychologist—Open Day and Night."

The real meaning of this is found in the fact that we are now able to use psychology as a guide or test in a thousand and one practical matters. In the old days there was no way of knowing what a man could do except by trying him out. Now we don't have to do this at all. We merely measure the shape of his head and see whether, by native intelligence he can, immediately and offhand, pronounce TH backward, or count the scales of a goldfish. This method has been applied for many years in the appointment of generals in the Chinese army, but with us it is new.

The Intelligence Test

In other words, the intelligence test has come to us as one of the first fruits of the new psychology. In practically every walk of life, this bright little device is now being introduced as a means of finding out what people don't know, and for what particular business they are specially unfitted.   Many persons, it now appears, go through life without being able to distinguish colors, or to arrange equilateral triangles into a tetrahedron, or to say the alphabet backwards. Indeed, some persons of this sort have in the past gone clear through and got away with it. They could hardly do so now.   And yet incompetent persons of this kind used often to occupy positions of trust, and even to handle money.

Let us see then what the intelligence test means.

If we wish to realize how slipshod is the thinking of persons in apparently sound mental condition, we have only to ask any man of our acquaintance how much is 13 times 147.   The large probability is that he doesn't know.   Or let us ask any casual acquaintance how many cubic centimeters there are in the Woolworth Building, and his estimate will be found to be absurdly incorrect.   The man, in other words, lacks observation.   His mind has never

41

been trained to form an accurate judgment.

Compare with this the operation of the trained, keener mind such as is being fashioned by the new psychology. This man, or shall we say this *mind,* for he deserves to be called it, walks down the street with his eye alert and his brain active. He notes the cubic contents of the buildings that he sees. He can tell you if you ask him (or even if you don't) the numbers of the taxicabs which he has passed, or overtaken, in his walk. He can tell you what proportion of red-haired men have passed him in a given time; how many steps he has taken in going a hundred yards; and how many yards he has walked in a given number of steps.

In other words, the man is a *thinker.* For such a man the intelligence test has no terrors. I questioned a man of this sort the other day. I said, "You have been in such and such an apartment building, have you not?" He answered, with characteristic activity of mind, "Yes." "And did you on entering such and such a hall in the building observe such and such a goldfish in such and such a bowl?" Judge my surprise when he told me that he had not only observed it, but had counted its scales and given it a peanut.   My readers, moreover, will readily believe me when I say that the man in question is the head of one of the biggest corporations in the city.   No one else could have done it.

But for persons who lack the proper training and habits of observation the intelligence test acts as a ruthless exterminator of incompetence. The point of it is, I repeat, that it is aimed not at eliciting the things which, from the very routine of our life itself, we are certain we know, but at those things which we ought to know but don't.

Here are a few little samples of what I mean, taken from the actual test questions used by one of our leading practical psychologists:

Intelligence Test for Bank Managers

1. Can you knit?
2. Name your favorite flower.
3. Which is the larger end of a safety pin?
4. How many wheels has a Pullman car?

5. If a spider wants to walk from the top corner of a room to the bottom corner farthest away, will he follow the angular diameter of the floor, or will his path be an obese tabloid?

It is the last question, I may say, which generally gets them. Already four of the principal bank managers in New York have lost their positions over it.

Let us put beside this from the same source another interesting set of questions:

Intelligence Test for Hospital Nurses

1. What is the difference between a Federal Reserve note and a Federal Reserve Bank note?
2. Suppose that a general buoyancy had led you to expand beyond what you considered prudent, and you felt that you must deflate, what would you take in first?

I may say that of seventeen trained nurses only *one* was able to answer these questions, especially No. 2, without wandering from the essential meaning; even the odd one hardly counted, as she turned out to be engaged to a bank teller.

Still more striking is the application of the intelligence test to the plain manual occupations. The worker fulfils, let us admit, his routine duty. But we have to ask, is this all that we have a right to demand from him? No. If the man is to be really competent, his mind ought to have a reach and an outlook which go beyond the mechanical operations of his job. I give an example:

Intelligence Test for Marine Engineers

1. Are you inclined to sympathize with Schiaparelli's estimate of Dante's *Divina Commedia?*
2. Luigi Pulci, it has been said, voices the last strains of the age of the troubadours. Do you get this?
3. Alfieri must always be regarded rather as the last of the *cinquecentisti* than as the first of the moderns. How do you stand on that?

Let us put beside this as an interesting parallel the following:

Intelligence Tests for Professors of Comparative Literature

1. How much pressure per square inch of surface do you think a safe load to carry?

2. Suppose that, just as you were getting to work, you got trouble somewhere in your flow of gas, so that that set up a back-firing in your tubes, would you attribute this to a defect in your feed?

3. Suppose that you were going along late at night at moderate speed, and properly lighted up, and you saw a red light directly in front of you, would you stop or go right on?

From all of which it appears that by means of the Intelligence Test we have now an infallible means of knowing just what a man amounts to. If we want to know whether or not an applicant is suited for a job we have only to send him to the laboratory of a practicing psychologist, and we can find out in fifteen minutes all about him. How vastly superior this is to the old and cumbersome methods of inquiring into a young man's schooling, and into his family, and reading personal letters of recommendation, can hardly be exaggerated. Let me quote as a typical example the case which I have just mentioned, that of letters of recommendation. Compare the old style and the new.

*Old-fashioned Letter of Recommendation Given to a
Young Man Seeking a Position in the Milling Business.*

To Messrs. Smith, Brown & Co.

Dear Sirs,

I should like to recommend to you very cordially
my young friend Mr. O'Hagan. I have known him
since his boyhood, and can assure you that he is an
estimable young man who has had a good schooling
and is willing to work. When I add that he was
raised right here in Jefferson County, and that his
mother was one of the McGerrigles, I feel sure that
you will look after him.

We have had an open fall here, but a good spell of
cold has set in since New Year's.

Very faithfully,

. . . .

*New-Fashioned Letter of Estimation as Supplied by
a Psychological Laboratory Expert*

Messrs. Smith, Brown & Co.

Dear Sirs,

This certifies that I have carefully examined Mr.
O'Hagan in my laboratory for fifteen minutes and
submitted him to various measurements and tests, with
a view to estimating his fitness for the Milling Busi-

ness. He measures 198 centimeters from end to end, of which his head represents 7.1 per cent. We regard this as too large a proportion of head for a miller. His angle of vision is 47, which is more than he will need in your business. We applied various stimuli to the lobes of his neck and got very little reaction from him. We regret to say that he does not know what 17 times 19 is; and we further found that, after being in our laboratory for fifteen minutes, he had failed to notice the number of panes in the windows.

On the whole, we think him better suited for social service or university work or for the church than for a position of responsibility.

Very truly,

. . . .

P. S. We enclose our statement of account for 17 tests at $5.00 per test.

The value of the system, however, does not stop even at this point. It is proving itself an invaluable aid in weeding out incompetent men who have perhaps escaped detection for many years. For example, a firm in Kansas were anxious to judge of the selling power of their salesmen. An intelligence test applied to their staff showed that *not a single one knew how to sell anything.* The firm had been misled for years by the mere fact that these men were successfully placing orders. A furniture factory in Grand Rapids submitted seventy-one of their employees to the test to see what they knew about furniture: it appeared that *they knew nothing about it.* One of the Kalamazoo Celery companies, anxious to develop the Psychology of Growing Celery, instituted a searching test of their gardeners. It appeared that only four of them had ever heard of psychology and only one of them could spell it. Yet here were men who had been professing to grow celery for twenty years. Instances such as these show how far from perfect is our industrial system. Nor will it ever be improved until sweeping intelligence tests and wholesale dismissals have put it on a new basis.

The Psychology of the Animal Mind

The sad truth is that as yet most of us do not know how to think. We think we think, but we don't.

Nor can we begin thinking until we are prepared to begin all over again and build up our
thought-process from its basis up. Herein lies
the peculiar importance of Animal Psychology
in the new wave of mentality.

Already the ground has been broken. Careful investigations of the thought-complex of the
hen, the worm, and the bee have revealed to the
world something of the wonderful mentality
that was formerly rudely classed as "instinct."
We now know that the bee could not construct
her honeycomb in the particular form which she
uses had she not some knowledge, however
modest, of the mathematical law of the maxi-
mum cubic content. Where she got it we do not
as yet know. But we hope to find out. Our psychological investigators are sitting among the
bees, following the hens, and associating with
the worms, and adding daily to our store of
knowledge.

My own researches in this direction are not
of wide extent. But I have endeavored to fit
myself for discussing the subject by undertaking
the study of one particular animal. I make

here no claim to originality of method, and readily admit that my researches are based upon—I may say, are imitated from—the best models of work in this direction. I selected as my subject the common Hoopoo, partly because no one had investigated the Hoopoo before, and partly because good fortune threw the opportunity in my way.

In other words, the observations which I have carried on in regard to the mentality and habits of the Hoopoo fall within that large portion of the new mentality which deals with the mind of animals. I should be ungrateful if I did not express my obligation to the authors of *The Play of Animals, The Behavior of the Toad, The Love Affairs of the Lobster,* and other well-known manuals of this class. But, so far as I am aware, I am the first to subject the Hoopoo to the same minute scrutiny which has been so successfully applied to the bee, the garden worm, and the iguanadon.

My acquaintance with the Hoopoo herself I owe to the fortunate fact that beside my house is an empty brick yard devoid of grass, occupied only with sand, litter, and broken stone—in short, a tempting spot for the entomologist.

It was while sitting on a brick in the empty brickyard, occupied, I fear, with nothing better than counting the grains of sand in a wagon load that had been dumped upon the ground, that I first saw the Hoopoo. She was making her way in the leisurely fashion that is characteristic of her, from one tiny pebble to another, daintily crossing the minute rivulets and ravines of the broken soil with that charm which is all hers. The glorious occasion was not to be lost. As hastily as I could, I made my way back to the house to bring my notebook, my pencil—without which my notebook could be but an aggravation—and my lens. Alas! by the time I had returned the Hoopoo had disappeared. I resolved henceforth to be of a greater prudence. Blaming myself for my lack of preparedness, I took care next night to sleep with my lens in bed with me so as to be ready at the earliest dawn to proceed to the brickyard.

The first beams of day saw me seated upon the same brick, my lens ready at hand, my notebook on my knee and my pencil poised in the air. But alas! my hopes were destined to be dashed to the ground. The Hoopoo did not appear.

The entomologist, however, must be patient. For five successive mornings I found myself seated on the brick in eager expectation. No result. But on the sixth morning there flashed through my mind one of those gleams of inductive reasoning which make the entomologist what he is. It occurred to me with such force as to make me wonder why it had not occurred to me with such force before, that on the first occasion I had seen the Hoopoo at *ten o'clock in the morning*. On all the other occasions I had sat on the brick at *four in the morning*. The inference was obvious. The Hoopoo does not get up until ten.

To wait until ten o'clock was the work of a moment. With renewed expectation, I found myself seated on the brick at the very moment when the shadow thrown by the morning sun from behind the chimney of a nearby factory indicated to me that it was ten o'clock. With a beating heart I watched the shadow steal across the ground. Alas! I was doomed again to failure. Ten o'clock came and passed and no sign of the Hoopoo greeted my anxious eye. I was just about to leave the place in despair and to select for my researches some animal less erratic than the Hoopoo, such as the horse, the boa-constrictor, or the common kangaroo, when a thought flashed through my mind calculated to turn my despair into a renewed anticipation. Six days—so it now suddenly occurred to me—had elapsed. One more would make seven. Seven days in a week. The inexorable logic was complete. The Hoopoo must appear once a week. The day of her first appearance had been Sunday. To-morrow she would come again.

The reader may imagine in what an agony of expectation I waited till next day. Spasms went through me when I thought of what the morrow might or might not bring. But this time I was not doomed to disappointment. Seated on my brick at the precise hour of ten, and watching the moving shadow, I became

54

suddenly aware that the Hoopoo had appeared
and was moving daintily over the dusty ground.
There was no doubt of her identity. My eye
dwelt with delight on the beautiful luster of
her carapace and the curvical appearance of her
snortex. Her antennæ gracefully swept the
air before her while the fibulæ with which her
feet were shielded traced a feathery pattern in
the dust. Hastily taking out my stop-watch, I
timed her. She was moving at the rate of the
tenth part of a centimeter in the twentieth of a
second. Her general direction was north-
north-west. But here entered an astounding
particularity which I am as yet unable to explain. The direction in which the Hoopoo was
moving was *exactly reversed from that of the
previous week.*

I determined now to test the intelligence of
the Hoopoo. Taking a small piece of stick,
I placed it directly across her path. *She
stepped over it.* I now supported the same
piece of stick by elevating it, still lying in the
Hoopoo's path, on two small pebbles. *She
went under it.* I next placed both stick and

stones together so as to form what must have appeared a formidable barrier directly in her path. *She went around it.* I now varied my experiment. With the blade of my knife I dug, directly in the path of the moving animal, a hole which must have appeared to her a considerable cavity. *She jumped across it.*

I need not, however, recite in detail the series of experiments which I carried out on this and the following Sunday mornings. I tested the Hoopoo in accordance with all the latest intelligence tests of animal life. And in every test she acquitted herself not only with credit but with distinction. I lifted her up with blades of grass, carried her to a distance of fifty yards and set her down again, to see if she could walk home (which she did), and fed her with minute particles of farraginous oatcake soaked in champagne. The result of my experiments show her to be right up in the front class of animal psychology, along with the ant, the bee, and the filipino.

In short if I wished to summarize the results

of my scientific labours on the Hoopoo and to set them down as an addition to human knowledge, on a par with most of our new discoveries in regard to the behaviour and psychology of animals, I should formulate them as follows:

1. When the Hoopoo is unable to step over anything, she walks round it.
2. The Hoopoo will drink water when she has to, but only when she has to, but she will drink champagne whether she has to or not.
3. The religious belief of the Hoopoo is dim.

Had the Hoopoo lived a great career would have opened up in front of her. Alas! she did not. An attempt to see whether the Hoopoo could eat gravel proved disastrous. But she at least lived long enough to add one more brilliant page to the growing literature of insect life.

I cannot but feel a sense of personal loss as I sit now in the solitude of the sunlit brickyard, listening to the hum of the zocataquil and the drone of the probiscus and the sharp staccato note of the jimjam.

The Human Memory

Try My System and You will never Forget it

But I turn not without a feeling of reluctance from the memory of the Hoopoo and the subject of animal psychology to another aspect of the human mind now very much in the foreground of interest. I refer to Memory.

I gather from the back pages of the magazines, which are the only ones that I ever read, that there seems to be a great demand for the strengthening of the human memory. A great many "systems of memory" are now being placed upon the market, and these systems, I am delighted to find, involve no strain upon the brain, can be acquired at an expenditure of only four minutes' time each day, resemble play rather than work, and are forwarded to any part of the United States or Canada for fifty cents.

Persons who are not satisfied with the treat-

58

ment may write and say so if they don't forget to do so. In short any one who cares to have it, can now acquire a memory as prehensile as a monkey's tail.

This is indeed a boon. After all, what is so distressing as a failing memory? Any reader of this book can tell for himself whether he is in the first stage of the collapse of memory by asking himself whether he has any difficulty in recalling the names of the people he meets on the street. Does the reader find himself greeted two or three times a week and compelled to say:—

"Excuse me, I seem to know your face, and there's something familiar about the droop of your head, and the silly expression of your features and that asinine way in which you lean forward on your feet but I can't recall your name."

That however is only the first stage. A little later on, unless the memory is attended to, and toned up by a system, it goes into a further lapse in which the victim thus accosted on the street is only able to answer:—

"Excuse me. I can't recall your name. I

59

don't remember your face. I never saw your clothes. I don't recollect your voice. If I ever saw you I have forgotten it. If I ever knew you, it has left no impression. Tell me frankly, are you one of my relations or just one of my best friends?"

After which it is very humiliating to have the stranger remind him of the simple fact that he was at the Schenectady High School with him only thirty-five years ago.

But the loss of memory as to names and faces is only a part of the evil. Many people find that as they grow older they lose their memory for words, for passages from books, for pieces of poetry familiar since childhood. The reader may test his own power of memory by completing if he can the following:—

"The boy stood on the burning deck
    Whence,——"

Let us ask "whence what?" and "in what direction?", "why was the deck burning?" and "why had the boy selected it for standing on?" Or this again:—

"Under the spreading chestnut tree,
    The village smithy stands,
    The smith,———"

Now then, quite frankly, what about the Smith? Can you give any idea of his personal appearance. What about his hands—eh what?

I may say at once that any reader who finds himself unable to recall poems of this class, or to name the branches of the Amazon, or to remember who it was that borrowed a dollar from him at bridge, is in a bad way and had better take treatment at once.

It is to meet this very kind of difficulty that I have been working out a system of memory. As yet it is only in a fragmentary shape, but even as it is, it may be found of use for certain purposes.

I will take a very familiar and very important case—the question of how to remember the delegates at a convention. All of us nowadays have to attend conventions of one kind or another—conventions of Furniture Men, or Rubber Men, or Stone Men, or Cement Men,

Gas Men, Air Men,—any kind of men.   And at every convention the delegate from Grand Rapids, Michigan, looks exactly like the delegate from Miami, Florida, and from Iksquak, Ungava.   Is there, one asks, any way by which one can remember the name of a peculiar delegate? Yes, I think, it can be done.

In my system in such a problem as this we proceed on the method of Infinite Verification. Put in simple language this means that if you say a thing over often enough presently you may remember it.   Thus if a delegate is introduced to you under the name of Mr. Louis Barker of Owen Sound, Ontario, as soon as he has been presented you must say:

"Pardon me, I am not sure that I have the name right?"

"Louis Barker."

"Ah, thank you, Mr. Barker, and from where did you say?"

"From Owen Sound."

"Oh, yes,—and I don't know if I got your Christian name?"

"Louis."

"Oh, certainly, and what did you say was your surname?"

"Barker."

"Yes, exactly, and from what town do you come, Mr. Barker?"

"From Owen Sound."

"Ah, to be sure and you said it was in Alberta."

"No, in Ontario."

"In Ontario! Of course, how stupid of me, and,—pardon me, I want to get it right,— did you say that your name was Lloyd or Tomlinson? For the moment I can't remember which."

When you hear two or more people going through this kind of conversation you may be sure that they are memory experts, and that they are paying fifty cents a week for memory lessons,—or they ought to.

At any rate there is no doubt that if that kind of question and answer is repeated often enough you will presently retain with absolute distinctness the recollection that the man's name is Louis Barker,—either that or William Baker.

And just at the time when you have got this established he himself will turn to you and say:

"Excuse me, I am afraid I am rather stupid, but did you say that your name was Edward Peterson or Lionel Jennings?"

It has to be observed however that even when this much has been accomplished you still may not be able to remember the delegate's face. That is another question. Science has not yet gone far enough to tell us whether it is possible to remember delegates' faces at conventions.

Such cases, however, are relatively simple. I turn to the more difficult problem of how to remember telephone numbers. Everybody knows how provoking it is when we cannot remember whether our best friend's telephone number is 4821 or 4281,—or just possibly 8241, or even 8421,—with a faint suspicion that it may be 2841 or,—stop a bit—2481. It seems a shame to remember it so nearly as

64

that—in fact, within a few thousands—and yet not get it.

The best solution, no doubt, is to associate only with people who have reasonable telephone numbers such as 9999 or 0000. Failing that, one must fall back on some kind of mnemonic device. Now in the case of numbers a great deal can be done by what we call technically the principle of association. This means that, after all, everything must in a way be like something else, and that even the oddest collection of figures are connected by some link or association with others more simple.

For example, a friend of mine told me that he had great difficulty in remembering his telephone number which was 2937-J. I drew his attention to the simple fact that 29 is only one short of thirty and that 37 is only three short of forty and that J is the next letter before K. After that the thing was absurdly easy.

A similar difficulty presented itself in another case where the telephone number was 4754. But after turning it over in my mind I realized that 47 is the highest prime number above 41 and that 54 would be the next if it were 53 instead of 54. Add to this that the number 4754 itself is nothing other than the square root of 22,600,516 and the problem is solved.

It may be objected that this form of memory work is open only to people of a mathematic mind—such as actuaries, astronomers, and the employees of a cash register company. Other people may prefer a form of association dealing rather with facts than with figures. In this connection I may quote the case of a man whose telephone number was 1066 and who was able to remember it by noticing that it represents the date of the Norman Conquest. This is capable of a wide application. If your telephone number is 2986 connect it at once with the fall of the Ming dynasty in China; if it is 3843, that is obviously the date of the death of Amenhotep the First and so on. In short, whatever your number is you have but to look it up in a book of history, connect an event with it, learn the event, memorize the date, and the thing is done. In such a case be careful not to

66

say to the operator: "Give me the landing of the Pilgrim fathers, Uptown-W."

Here is a more intricate problem in which the student of memory may surprise his friends with the brilliance of his performance,—I refer to the power to memorize a long and disconnected series of names. The best illustration or at least the most familiar, is the series of the names of the Presidents of the United States in order of office.

When we apply the principle of association to this, what appears an almost insuperable task is easily overcome. Take the first link in the chain. We want to remember that after Washington comes Adams. Can it be done? Yes, by association. We connect with the word Washington anything that it suggests, and then something that that suggests, and so on till we happen to get to Adams—

Washington evidently suggests washing.

Washing evidently suggests laundry.

Laundry evidently suggests the Chinese.

The Chinese evidently suggest missionaries.

Missionaries evidently suggest the Bible.

The Bible begins with Adam.

How ridiculously simple!

In conclusion I may say that if any reader of this book will send me fifty cents, I will either (a) forward to him by post my entire system of memory, or (b) send him back his fifty cents, or (c) keep his fifty cents and say nothing about it. If his memory is so weak as to need a system he will have forgotten his fifty cents anyway.

III

THE HUMAN BODY—ITS CARE AND PREVENTION

III.—The Human Body—Its Care and Prevention

HAVING put the human mind where it belongs, or at least placed it where it can do no harm, we shall proceed in the present chapter to deal with the human body in her various aspects. Most readers will admit —except those who are complete nuts—that, with the single exception of the mind and the soul, there is nothing so important as the body. If we had no body it is doubtful if we could get along. Without the body most of us, if not all of us, would feel lost. Life itself would lose much of its elasticity, and even the most optimistic would be oppressed with a sense of emptiness.

Under such circumstances it is obvious that the care and use of the body is a matter of prime importance. We must study the question of how we are to treat it. What will be the best food to give it? What would it like to eat? Does it care for fruit and nuts? Are eggs good for it? In short, the thoughtful man when he sits down to eat will not merely consider his own personal likes and dislikes, but will remember that he must look after his body.

The same is true of exercise. The wise man when he goes out for a walk will take his body along with him. Air is good for it: and he will see to it that his body is always properly warmed, housed, and cleaned. It is not too much to say that the proper care of the body has a close connection with the health.

To maintain this care there is needed a continued and anxious personal attention. The thing must not be left to subordinates. The man of sense will keep up a minute and unceasing examination of his skin, his hair, and his whole exterior. If he drops a hair he should pick it up at once: one of the follicles at its base may have given way or perhaps the fall of the hair may mean that he is in the incipient

stage of scatalosis, or mange.   If so, he ought
to inform himself of it without delay.

Nor is it only the external aspect of the body
that should be an object of continuous attention.   The same thing is true of the interior,
or what we may call medically, the inside.
The prudent man especially as he reaches middle life, will keep a watchful eye turned on his
inside.   Are his ducts functioning?   How is
his great colon?   And the shorter, or semi-
colon, what about that?   Is there an easy
flow of nitric acid from the œsophagus to the
proscenium?   If not, what is stopping it: has
perhaps a lot of sand or mud made its way into
the auditorium?   Are the sebaceous glands in
what one might call efficient working condition,
and are the valves of the liver revolving as they
ought to?   Are the eyes opening and shutting
properly, and is the lower jaw swinging on its
hinges as it should?   In short, the man of
discretion will go over himself each day and
tap himself with a small hammer to see that
his body is functioning as it ought to.

This care of the body and, particularly this

attention to food, is a thing of very recent growth. It belongs only with the era in which we live and with the development of the advertising sections of the metropolitan press and with the invention of scenic advertising along the lines of our great railways. It is amazing how careless our ancestors were in this respect. The early pioneers who cut down the forests and settled the farm lands of North America never seem to have taken any exercise. They knew nothing of the value of deep breathing or of the advantage of lifting the left knee up to the chest five times every morning before breakfast.

As to food, the mental state of our ancestors was appalling. They were ignorant of vitamines, calories, and of the proper proportion of ferruginous and diaphanous elements in diurnal diet. They ate pancakes, oatcakes, johnnycakes, and other albuminous integers without realizing that in so doing they were increasing their consumption of protein without any corresponding balance of nitrogen. They seem to have eaten meats, pies, ham sandwiches, doughnuts, and dog biscuits under the silly impression that such things are food. We have only to open a modern scientific book on *Diet and What it Does to Us* to realize that they are not. These things may satisfy the appetite and distend the stomach and create a distressing hallucination of happiness, but they are not food. In the true sense, food will be found to consist of certain chemical products including nitrogen, carbon (such as common coal), cement, glue, and other lifegiving elements. To all of these we now give the name vitamines, to indicate that without them life is not possible, or, if possible at all, is too dull to count. But to get at the root of the matter we must turn back to the beginning of our analysis and must proceed to build up a science of food.

The Science of Food

The first thing we have to do is to obtain a scientific view of the nature of food and to answer the question why do we eat and what will happen if we don't. Most people have never stopped to ask themselves why they eat and could not give a satisfactory reason why they do so. From the medical point of view the problem is not so simple as it sounds, but we may, in an approximate way, answer the question by saying that if we did not eat we should lose tone and elasticity, there would be a lowering of buoyancy, our blood would slacken, our stomach would sink, and our clothes would come unbuttoned. Granted then that we are satisfied with the answer to our first question and admit, perhaps regretfully, that we must eat, we are confronted with the second inquiry, how much should we eat and when have we eaten enough? Here again science is able to give us a definite answer. There are certain plain and obvious symptoms which indicate to the trained eye that we have eaten enough. The distention of the stomach, as notified by the stretching and cracking of the skin, the bulging of the eyes, and the inability to move the jaws, should warn us that it is time to rise from the table—if we can. Some specialists, however, hold that even when this stage has been reached a more complete repletion can still be secured by the infiltration of buckwheat pancakes and maple syrup. This, however, is a technical matter of secondary importance. The main factor is that after a certain point is reached a general feeling of compactness, of solidification, of unification of the whole body sets in and informs us that if we like we can stop eating without harm.

This much established, we pass to the much more delicate inquiry what can we eat and, if we do, how can we digest it? This inquiry we cannot undertake, however, until we are prepared to understand what it is that happens, medically and scientifically, to our food. The process runs thus. The food is first introduced into the mouth, where it is thrown violently back and forward, beating with great force against the cheeks: by this means it is folded into a ball and thrown to the œsophagus, which catches it, spins it round, and hurls it with a splash into the stomach. In this organ it is further pounded, pulverized, kicked, and bruised. Reduced thus into its elements, the food is divided, some of it passes into the liver, some into the heart, some into the eyes, causing them to bulge, while some again goes back into the face, causing it to swell and expand until its temperature reaches the boiling point and is carried off in the form of steam. The food not thus used is thrown by the stomach into the tetrahedron and disappears.

So far so good. We have now to ask what particular substances are those which present to us the proper food values. Science tells us that food consists of the following things: the class of substances called proteins, such as ordinary paste, glue (as found on the back of postage stamps), shoeblacking, including tan-polish, etc., etc.; the whole class known as carbons, such as common coal, burnt sticks, lampblack, and so on; a number of gases, to include nitrogen, hydrogen, sulphuric acid as found in eggs, and so forth. In addition to these principal articles of diet, the body needs, if it is to maintain a perfect health, a certain quantity of phosphorus, lime, old iron, sugar, gin, cement, rust, beans, mud, and other bone-making elements.

Computation by Calories

For a perfect science of food we need, however, more than a mere list of the food ingredients. We must have some form of relative measurement of computation. Modern science supplies this in the form of the calory, one of the newest and brightest discoveries in the art of eating. A calory (which is derived from the Greek *calico*, I eat) means the amount of units of heat which a food constituent imparts to the body. Thus when we eat a pound of beefsteak we are aware of a growing sensation of heat; on eating a second pound we are hotter still; on eating the third pound our latent heat, if it were not carried off in the form of a cloud rising from the face, would result in serious inconvenience and perhaps in a liquefaction of the kidneys. In other words, we should be at the boiling point.

Experience shows that a pound of beefsteak contains 800 calories; a pound of sausages contains 1600 calories; while coal tar, although it is nearly 500 times sweeter than sugar, contains

79

no calories at all. This is why we do not eat coal tar. On the other hand, various articles of diet which are very commonly neglected are very rich in calories: of these we may mention Brazil nuts, popcorn, timothy hay, spinach, raw oats, and grass seed.

We are now in a position to indicate the general tenor of a balanced diet. We may set it down somewhat as follows:

BREAKFAST MENU
(For an adult)
100 calories of nitrogen dioxide
100 calories (ten pounds) of popcorn
100 calories (one packet) of bird seed.

It will be found that any adult in good condition who eats this breakfast will rise from it with a sense of lightness and volubility quite lacking after his usual diet.

BREAKFAST MENU
(For a child)
100 calories of hay
1 pint of sour milk (very rich and swarming with vitamines)

2 pounds of beefsteak (high value in carbohydrates)
1 cake of soap.

Let us try a slight variation.

AVIATOR'S BREAKFAST
(Before Flying)
Hydrogen (400 calories)
Popcorn (half a bushel)

AVIATOR'S DINNER
(After Flying)
1 pound of cement
3 calories of iron
1 can of stewed lead
with perhaps a crab-apple.

Anybody with a constructive mind will readily see how easy and simple it becomes, when once we have a proper knowledge of food values, to put together a suitable diet or menu for any kind of occasion. It is needless to multiply examples. But a few typical illustrations may serve to develop our meaning to the saturation point. Thus:

81

MENU FOR ANNUAL LUNCHEON
OF AN ARTISTS' LEAGUE

Hors d'Œuvre—Air

Soup—Nitrogen

Fish—Gasoline

Pièce de Résistance—100 Cal. Spinach

Dessert—More Spinach

Having now arranged a perfect diet adaptable to all places and times, our next concern is with the problem of how to digest it. Can we do it? We can. Modern science is able to state confidently that food if properly combined and put into the body can be digested: in fact, this is one of the great triumphs of modern science.

In past ages, though it was not known at the time, many of the principal troubles of the world arose from indigestion. We read of the deep melancholy of Dante and of how he would sit brooding for hours. This was indigestion. If Dante had taken a few calories of liquid air and a plate of popcorn every morning he would never have felt this. We read of the terrible restlessness all over Europe which led to the first Crusade: again indigestion; if Peter the Hermit and his followers had known how to take a few suitable exercises on the floor of the bathroom every morning they would never have started for Jerusalem.

In other words, the secret of digestion lies in exercise; not taken in the rude fashion of earlier times on horseback and with hounds and in such ways, but taken on the floor of the bathroom while lying on the stomach. We now know—everybody knows who reads in the press—that exercise of this kind can be so contrived as to be a form of play, of mere skittishness. The person exercising jumps out of his bed of a morning, rushes to the bathroom, throws himself on the floor, and in ten minutes of playfulness sets himself up in energy for the day. Without wishing to injure the sale of any of the numerous methods of exercise already on the market, I venture here to put in my own system, merely as a sample, more or less typical, of what is being achieved in this respect.

Daily Exercise on the Floor

In taking these exercises the operator should be dressed in pajamas and the exercises should be performed on the floor of a bathroom. This last is a point of especial importance. The floor of the bathroom—according to all published directions—is the only safe place in which to take these exercises. They should *not* be taken on the floor of a ball room, nor on the table of a dining room.

Course No. I.

This course is specially designed for persons in middle life anxious to get rid of obesity, melancholy, and taciturnity.

Movement No. 1. Standing on the ball of the left foot, wave the right foot three times smartly around the head, at the same time shouting, Hoorah! Hoorah! Hoorah!

Movement No. 2. Do it again.

Movement No. 3. Again.

Movement No. 4. Once more, this time shouting Ha! Ha! Ha! as the foot whirls round the head.

84

Movement No. 5. Standing in an easy attitude, pass the right arm below and behind the right knee so as to bring it round above and beyond the left shoulder, at the same time rapidly revolving the body to the right and elevating the left foot so as to pivot on the right heel.

Movement No. 6. Keep on spinning.

Movement No. 7. Reverse.

Movement No. 8. Go into low gear.

Movement No. 9. Stop.

Movement No. 10. Turn a couple of handsprings downstairs and sit down to breakfast.

Ten minutes of this kind of play taken every day will keep obesity at arm's length indefinitely.

Course No. II.

(*For Business Men.*)

This course is so designed that it can be taken in the office itself at intervals between signing checks, closing deals, and taking in money. There is no need, in short, for the business man to get out of his swivel chair while doing these movements.

Movement No. 1.   Move the ears gently back and forward.

Movement No. 2.   Light a large cigar and breathe very deeply in such a way as alternately to draw the smoke into the cavity of the mouth and expel it.

Movement No. 3.   While still continuing No. 2, place the feet upon a stool or chair within easy distance, fold the hands across the stomach, and close the eyes.

Movement No. 4.   Keep on.

Movement No. 5.   Let the cigar fall sideways into an ashtray, place the head in a drooping position, draw a handkerchief over the cranium and remain in this posture for half an hour.

Movement No. 6.   Pretend to snore.

Movement No. 7.   Come smartly to an attitude of alacrity, remove the handkerchief, pick the cigar up out of the ashtray, whirl round three times on the swivel chair, ring for the stenographer, and start a new deal, at the same time moving the ears back and forward with rapidity.

So much then for our ideas of what human food ought to be and what it ought to contain. Let us now ask—because we must keep on asking something—is it possible to obtain any simple prepared food which contains all the required ingredients in exactly the right proportion, and has such a food ever been discovered? We answer it is and it has. This marvelous achievement of science was consummated in the discovery of *Humpo,* the perfect breakfast food obtainable at all grocers. I do not know whether our readers have ever heard of *Humpo.* They may have lived so far out of the main current of modern thought that they know nothing of it. But at least they have read in the advertising pages of the press of various preparations similar yet inferior. By the way, all readers should be cautioned never to accept these inferior preparations. No matter what persuasion or blandishment may be used, they should answer, "No, I want *Humpo.*" They must never accept the statement that any preparation is equal to it. To

87

any such insinuation they must say with the utmost firmness, "I insist on *Humpo*."

Students of this subject know how long and how eagerly the world had sought a perfect breakfast food. Benjamin Franklin is said to have said that if there had been a perfect breakfast food there would have been no Declaration of Independence. Napoleon at St. Helena often remarked that with a perfect breakfast food he would have won the battle of Waterloo; and Abraham Lincoln in his droll way once said that if he had a perfect breakfast food he wouldn't take any breakfast.

But for years the greatest scientists worked in vain. Sir Humphry Davy, Charles Darwin, and Thomas Huxley were compelled to abandon the problem. It remained for Dr. Oscar P. Kloonspotz to solve it. The picture of Dr. Kloonspotz may be seen in the advertising pages of any illustrated periodical. He is depicted in what is evidently his laboratory, shrouded by huge glass retorts, crucibles, test scales, and little heaps of various grains. The intensity of the expression of the doctor's face shows that at the moment when they photographed him he was in the very act of discovering *Humpo*.

It was his task to prepare a food product containing exactly the right amount of starch, mud, and phosphorus to supply the great life-giving elements with just enough amygdaloid to make it palatable. As soon as he had done this Dr. Kloonspotz—rightly called the Wizard of Food—gave his preparation to the world. It may be now had anywhere, put up in a sealed package, and sold for a nominal sum payable merely in money.

Great Moments in the History of Human Welfare.

The Discovery of "Balso" by the Wizard of the Adirondacks.

Undoubtedly the discovery of *Humpo* marked an era in human history. In fact, Dr. Kloonspotz, who is modesty itself, is reported to have said (his words are printed on the package): "a perfect breakfast means a perfect day."

The only other achievement in the history of human welfare that can be compared with the compounding of *Humpo* is the story of the discovery of *Balso*. What *Humpo* does for the well body, *Balso* does for the sick. The problem in this case was to find, not a substance which would maintain the body in health, but a remedy which should heal and restore the body in any and every form of illness. By this time no doubt all the world knows the story. Everybody who reads is familiar with the picture of the individual whom I designate the Wizard of the Adirondacks. This venerable man, looking like Father Time, wearing a flowing beard and dressed in a bath towel, is seen on the outside of the packet of *Balso* and elsewhere while engaged in stirring the contents of a huge iron pot. All around him is a setting of pine trees and rock in the fastnesses of the mountains. The whole scene breathes an aroma of the woods and of the life-giving balsam which must exist there. As the steam rises from the pot we realize that the Wizard is in the act of discovering his great remedy. The mind is almost staggered at the thought.

The remedy once found, the next problem was to give it an appropriate name. Such a name ought to be at once scientific and scholarly, and yet short enough to be cheap to print, and calculated to convey a certain hint, but not too much, of its possible connection with the balsam tree. With characteristic ingenuity the Wizard himself, after deep thought, invented the name *Balso,* under which the great remedy has since become famous all the world over. Readers, by the way, are warned that anything that is called something else is a different thing, and should be avoided like the pest. Unscrupulous dealers—and we know what *they* are—may try to sell us preparations purporting to be equal in curative property. But the reader has only to understand what *Balso* does to realize that there can be only one thing like it.

A word as to the properties of *Balso*. Let it first be distinctly understood that *Balso* has no connection whatever with the remedies and the treatments of the medical colleges. It stands on a much higher authority. The original secret of *Balso* comes from the Dog Rib Indians. It was perhaps known also to the Flat Heads and the Snub-Nosed Piutes and other great aborigines. Possibly the Hottentots used it. At any rate *Balso* is a "simple," and when we say that we reach our readers where they live.

The extraordinary advantage of *Balso* lies in the wide range of its use. In the first place, it undoubtedly heals all forms of bone disease when rubbed on the bones. For all internal complaints—especially those indicated by a sinking or depressed feeling, or a forlorn sensation, or by an inability to earn money—*Balso* effects an immediate cure. In these cases it is taken internally, by the pint. For diseases of the hair, such as complete baldness or lethargy of the scalp, a smart rubbing of *Balso* will work wonders; while for infantile complaints, such as croup, whoop, paresis, and so forth, the child should be rubbed with *Balso* and laid upon a shelf.

It is curious to think that if the Dog Rib Indians had all died, and if there had been no conservation of the great forests—but after all why think it?   The essential thing is that some day the jealousy and envy of the colleges will give way and this great remedy will come into its own.

The Secrets of Longevity and Perpetual Youth

Our readers—those of them who have arrived at this point of our discussion, and we are really not concerned with the others—will naturally interpose and say, "You have told us how the body may be sustained, renovated, and upholstered by means of systematic diet and exercise, and how it can be restored from vital or wasting disease, such as baldness, mange, and sinking of the stomach.   What we wish to know is how long can life be thus sustained and prolonged." If they do ask this our readers will receive a shock of surprise—in fact, we have been keeping this shock for them—when we say that there is no reason why they should not live as long as they care to. (This offer is restricted, of course, to readers of these pages; others must die as usual.) In other words, we must now know so much about longevity that we have practically arrived at the secret of living forever—or at any rate until death.

It may be of interest to show the way in which modern science has arrived at this conclusion. In the first place a great many actual cases of longevity have been examined and useful conclusions drawn from each. I will quote a few cases here—merely a few among thousands—such as help toward deductions in regard to the possibilities of old age. They are taken, as appears from the form in which they are written, from the columns of the daily papers, but each case has also been certified to either by a local minister of the Gospel or a notary public, or by a duly qualified hotelkeeper.

Case No. 1. (as reported in the *Daily Annalist,* Cedar Corners, Iowa.) "William Waterson celebrated his hundred and first birthday at his residence here at Cedar Corners. The old gentleman is still hale and hearty and celebrated the day by splitting two cords of wood. Mr. Waterson has been a water drinker all his life, having never tasted alcoholic spirits or tobacco." The inference here is obvious. Mr. Waterson's life has been preserved for the plain and evident reason that he drinks only water and never smokes. If he touches whiskey or cigarettes it will be all over with him.

We put beside this, however, a rather puzzling item which appears in the *Weekly News and Intelligencer,* Georgina Township, Ontario.

"Mr. Edward Easiest celebrated his one hundred and first birthday here at the home of his son surrounded by his grandchildren in the presence of a representative of the *Weekly Intelligencer* devoutly giving thanks to the Lord for his continued health and strength. Mr. Easiest has been a heavy smoker all his days and still relishes his glass of hot toddy compounded of rum, spices, and sugar."

Good old man! Can we blame him? And in any case it is clear that he owes his life to rum and tobacco. Indeed, what looks simple at first begins to appear more complicated. Compare this:

"Jarrets' Corners, N. Y. Cornelia Cleopatra Washington (colored) celebrated here her one hundred and tenth birthday yesterday. She remembers George Washington as a child." Plain enough she lived so long because she was colored. There seems no other reason.

Llanfydd, Wales (From the *Llanfydd Fyddist.*)

"Mrs. Llewellyn Owen, a resident of this town, celebrated her one hundred and fifth birthday yesterday. Mrs. Owen, who has lived in Wales since her childhood, a hundred and ten years ago, still retains all her faculties and maintains a keen interest in English politics, especially in the doings of Lloyd George whom she remembers a hundred years ago as a pupil in her father's school. Mrs. Owen talks interestingly of the great fire of London (which she remembers as a girl) and of the sailing of the Pilgrim Fathers, many of whom she knew. She doubts whether the Cabinet of the Labor Party in England contains men of the same caliber as the greatest men in history."

In this case without a doubt Mrs. Owen owes her life to her interest in English politics.   Indeed one observes many cases of this sort.

From examples such as these we see at once that there are certain things which conduce to perpetual youth, such as drinking nothing else throughout life but water, or nothing but rum as the case may be.   Total abstinence from tobacco undoubtedly prolongs life and so does excessive smoking.   But modern science has recently recognized that in the main what we call old age is a condition brought on by an insufficiency of sour milk in the system.   The discoveries of Dr. Menschnikoff have shown that sour milk is full of minute polyglots which, when let loose in the human body, effect a general restoration by removing all waste.   It is now proven beyond doubt that anybody who takes a gallon of sour milk night and morning can live forever.   The only question is—Is it worth it?

IV
THE PERFECT SALESMAN

A COMPLETE GUIDE TO BUSINESS

IV.—The Perfect Salesman
A Complete Guide To Business

I ADMIT at the outset that I know nothing direct, personal or immediate about business. I have never been in it. If I were told tomorrow to go out and make $100,000 I should scarcely know how to do it. If anybody showed me a man on the street and told me to sell him a municipal six per cent bond I shouldn't know how to begin: I wouldn't know how to "approach" him, or how to hold his interest, or how to make him forget his troubles, or how to clinch him, or strike him to the earth at the final moment.

As to borrowing money,—which is one of the great essentials of business,—I simply couldn't do it. As soon as I got across the steps of the bank I should get afraid,—scared that they would throw me out. I know, of course, from reading about it that this is mere silliness, that the bankers are there simply waiting to lend money,—just crazy to lend it.   All you have to do is to invite the general manager out to lunch and tell him that you want half a million dollars to float a big proposition (you don't tell him what it is,—you just say that you'll let him know later) and the manager, so I gather, will be simply wild to lend you the money.   All this I pick up from the conversations which I overhear at my club from men who float things.   But I couldn't do it myself: there's an art in it: to borrow money, big money, you have to wear your clothes in a certain way, walk in a certain way, and have about you an air of solemnity and majesty,—something like the atmosphere of a Gothic cathedral.   Small men like me and you, my dear reader, especially you, can't do it. We feel mean about it: and when we get the money, even if it is only ten dollars, we give ourselves away at once by wanting to hustle away with it too fast.   The really big man in this kind of thing can borrow half a million, button it up in his chest, and then draw on his gloves and talk easily about the League of Nations and the prospect of rain. I admit I couldn't do it. If I ever got that half a million dollars, I'd beat it out of the bank as fast as a cat going over a fence.

So, as I say, I make no pretensions to being a business man or to knowing anything about business. But I have a huge admiration for it, especially for big business, for the men at the top. They say that the whole railway business of this continent centres really in four men; and they say, too, that the whole money power of New York is really held by about six men; the entire forests of this country are practically owned by three men; the whole of South America, though it doesn't know it, is controlled by less than five men; and the Atlantic Ocean is now to all intents and purposes in the hands of a little international group of not more than seven and less than eight.

Think what it would mean to be one of those eight, or one of that four, or even, one or two of that three! There must be a tremendous fascination about it, to be in this kind of really

Big Business: to sit at a desk and feel one's great brain slowly revolving on its axis; to know that one's capacious mind was majestically turning round and round, and to observe one's ponderous intellect moving irresistibly up and down.

We cannot wonder, when we reflect on this, that all the world nowadays is drawn by the fascination of business. It is not the money that people want: I will acquit humanity of that: few people care for money for its own sake: it is the thought of what can be done with the money. "Oh, if I only had a million dollars!" I heard a woman say the other day on the platform of a social service meeting. And I could guess just what she meant,—that she would quit work and go to the South Sea Islands and play mah jong and smoke opium. I've had the same idea again and again.

Salesmanship and the Perfect Salesman

The most essential feature of modern business is, I imagine, salesmanship. My readers may not appreciate this at once,—they seldom seem to get anything readily,—and so I will explain some of the reasons which lead me to think so. Without salesmanship we could not sell anything. If we could not sell anything we might as well not make anything, because if we made things and couldn't sell them it would be as bad as if we sold things and couldn't make them.

Hence the most terrible danger that the world can face is that everybody will be buying things and nobody able to sell them. This danger of not selling anything, which used to threaten the world with disaster only a short time ago, is now being removed. Salesmanship, my readers will be glad to learn,—at least, if the miserable creatures ever get thrilled at anything,—is being reduced to a science. A great number of Manuals of Salesmanship are now being placed within reach of everybody and from these we can gather the essentials of the subject.

In the small space which it is here feasible to devote to the subject it is not possible to treat in an adequate way such a vast and important subject as modern salesmanship.   For complete information recourse should be had to any one of the many manuals to which I refer and which can be had at a trifling sum, such as ten dollars, or even more.   But we may indicate here a few of the principal points of salesmanship.

Personality of the Salesman

It is essential that the salesman should have charm.   If he wishes to sell anything,— let us say lead pipe for use in sewers and house drains,—he will find that what he needs most in selling is personal charm, a sort of indefinable manner, with just that little touch of noblesse which suggests the easy camaraderie of the menagerie.   In other words, he must diffuse wherever he goes, in selling sewer pipes, a sense of sunshine which makes the world seem a little brighter when he is gone.

In person the perfect salesman should be rather tall with a figure which suggests, to his customers, the outline of the Venus de Milo. According to the manuals of salesmanship he can get this figure by taking exercises every

106

morning on the floor of his hotel bedroom. But the discussion of that point has been undertaken already. Let us suppose him then with the characteristic figure of a Venus de Milo, or if one will of a Paduan Mercury, or of a Bologna sausage. We come, in any case, to the all important points of dress.

How Shall the Perfect Salesman Dress?

Every manual on the subject emphasizes the large importance of dress for the salesman. Indeed there is probably nothing which has a greater bearing on success and failure in the salesman than his dress. The well dressed man,—in selling, let us say, municipal bonds, has an initial advantage over the man who comes into his customer's store in tattered rags, with his toes protruding from his boots, unshaved and with a general air of want and misery stamped all over him. Customers are quick to notice these little things. But let the salesman turn up in an appropriate costume, bright and neat from head to foot and bringing with him something of the gladness of the early spring and the singing bird and the customer is immediately impressed in his favour.

One asks, what then should be the costume of the perfect salesman? It is not an easy question to answer. Obviously his costume must vary with the season and with the weather and with the time of day. One might suggest, however, that on rising in the morning the salesman should throw round him a light peignoir of yellow silk or a figured kimono slashed from the hips with pink insertions and brought round in a bold sweep to the small of the back. This should be worn during the morning toilet while putting the hair up in its combs, while adjusting the dickie and easing the suspenders. If breakfast is taken in the bedroom the liver and bacon may be eaten in this costume.

Breakfast over, the great moment approaches for the perfect salesman to get out upon the street. Here the daintiest care must be selected in choosing his dress. And here we may interpose at once a piece of plain and vigorous advice:—the simplest is the best. The salesman makes a great mistake who comes into his customer's premises covered with jewellery, with earrings in his ears and expensive bracelets on his feet and ankles. Nor should there be in the salesman's dress anything the least suggestive of immodesty. No salesman should ever appear with bare arms, or with his waistcoat cut so low as to suggest impropriety. Some salesmen, especially in the hardware business, are tempted to appear with bare arms, but they ought not to do it. For evening wear and for social recreation the case is different. When work is over the salesman in returning to his hotel may very properly throw on a georgette camisole open at the throat or a lace fichu with ear-flaps of perforated celluloid. But the salesman should remember that for the hours of business anything in the way of a luxurious or suggestive costume should be avoided. Unfortunately this is not always done. I have myself again and again noticed salesmen, especially in the hardware business where they take their coats off, to be wearing a suit calculated to reveal their figure round the hips and the lower part of the back in an immodest way.

All this kind of thing should be avoided. The salesman should select from his wardrobe (or from his straw valise) a suit of plain severe design, attractive and yet simple, good and yet bad, long and at the same time short, in other words, something that is expensive but cheap.

He should button this up in some simple way with just a plain clasp at the throat, agate perhaps or onyx, and then, having buttoned up all his buttons, but, mark me, not until then, he should go out upon the street prepared to do business.

Let any of my readers who doubts the importance of dress,—and some of them are nuts enough to doubt anything,—consider the following little anecdote of salesmanship. It is one that I selected from among the many little anecdotes of the sort which are always inserted in the manuals.

Anecdote of the Ill-Dressed Salesman

"A salesman in the middle west, whom we will call Mr. Blank, called upon a merchant, whom we will call Mr. Nut, and finding no difficulty in approaching him started in to show him his line with every hope of selling him. It should be explained that the line which Mr. Blank carried consisted of haberdashery, gents furnishings and cut-to-fit suits. Mr. Nut was evidently delighted with the samples and already a big pile of neckties, gents collarings, gents shirtings and gents sockings was stacked up on the counter and an order form for $375.-50 all ready to sign, when Mr. Nut noticed the salesman's own costume. Mr. Blank, who was a careless man in regard to dress though otherwise a man of intelligence, was wearing a low crowned Derby hat with a scooping brim over his ears, a celluloid collar and a dickie that was too small for him. His coat sleeves came only a little way below his elbows and plainly showed his cuffs, fastened with long steel clips to his undershirt. In other words, the man somehow lacked *class*. Mr. Nut put down his pen. 'I'm sorry, Mr. Blank,' he said, 'I can't buy from you. Your line is all right but you lack something, I can't just say what, but if I had to give it a name I should call it *tone*.' Blank, however, who was a man of resource, at once realized his error. 'One moment, Mr. Nut,' he said, 'don't refuse this order too soon.' With that he gathered up his valise and his samples and retreated to the back of the store behind a screen. In a few minutes he reappeared *dressed in his own samples*. The merchant, delighted in the change in Mr. Blank's appearance, kissed him and signed the order."

Approaching the Prospect

So much for the salesman's dress, a matter of great importance but still only a preliminary to our discussion. Let us suppose then our salesman, fully dressed, his buttons all adjusted and drawing well, his suspenders regulated and his dickie set well in place. His next task is to "approach" his customer.

All those who understand salesmanship are well aware this is the really vital matter. Everything depends on it. And nevertheless "approaching" the merchant is a thing of great difficulty. The merchant, if we may believe our best books on salesmanship, is as wary as a mountain antelope. At the least alarm he will leap from his counter ten feet in the air and rush to the top of his attic floor: or perhaps he will make a dive into his cellar where he will burrow his way among barrels and boxes and become completely hidden. In such a case he can only be dug out with a spade. Some merchants are even crafty enough to have an assistant or sentinel posted in such a way as to give the alarm of the salesman's approach.

How then can the salesman manage to get his interview with the merchant or, to use a technical term, to get next to his *prospect?* The answer is that he must "stalk" his prospect as the hunter stalks the mountain goat or the wild hog. Dressed in a becoming way he must circulate outside his prospect's premises, occasionally taking a peep at him through the window and perhaps imitating the song of a bird or the gentle cooing of a dove. Pleased with the soft note of the bird's song the prospect will presently be seen to relax into a smile. Now is the moment for the salesman to act. He enters the place boldly and says with a winning frankness, "Mr. Nut, you thought it was a bird. It was not. It was I. I am here to show you my line."

If the salesman has chosen his moment rightly he will win. The merchant, once decoyed into looking at the line, is easily landed. On the other hand, the prospect may refuse even now to see the salesman and the attack must begin again. This difficulty of getting the merchant to see the salesman even when close beside him and the way in which it can be overcome by perseverance is well illustrated by a striking little anecdote which I quote from a recent book on salesmanship. The work, I may say, is authoritative, having been written by a man with over thirty years of experience in selling hardware and perfumes in the middle southwest.

Anecdote of the Invisible Merchant

"A salesman whom we will call Mr. M.—" I should perhaps explain here the M. is not really his name but just an ingenious way of indicating him,—"while travelling in the interests of perfume in the middle southwest came to a town which we designate T. where he was most anxious to see a prospect whom we will speak of as P. Entering P.'s premises one morning M. asked if he could see P. P. refused. M. went out of the store and waited at the door until P. emerged at the noon hour. As soon as P. emerged M. politely asked if he could see him. P. refused to be seen. M. waited till night and then presented himself at P.'s residence. 'Mr. P.,' said M., 'can I see you?' 'No,' said P., 'you can't.' This sort of thing went on for several days, during which M. presented himself continually before P. who as continually refused to see him. M. was almost in despair,—"

Perhaps I may interrupt this little story a moment to beg my readers not to be too much oppressed by M.'s despair. In these anecdotes the salesmen are always in despair at the lowest point of the story. But it is only a sign that the clouds are breaking. I will beg my readers then,—if the poor simps have been getting depressed,—to cheer up and hear what follows:—

"M., we say, was almost in despair when an idea occurred to him. He knew that Mr. P. was a very religious man and always attended divine worship (church) every Sunday. Disguising himself, therefore, to look like one of the apostles, M. seated himself at one side of Mr. P.'s pew. Mr. P. mistaking him for St. Matthew, was easily induced, during the sermon, to look over M.'s line of perfume."

The above anecdote incidentally raises the important question how frank should the salesman be with his prospect. Should he go to the length of telling the truth? An answer to this is that frankness will be found to be the best policy. We will illustrate it with a little story taken from the experience of a young salesman travelling in the north southwest in the interest of brushes, face powder and toilet notions.

Anecdote of the Truthful Salesman

"A young salesman, whom we will indicate as Mr. Asterisk, travelling 'in' brushes and toilet supplies, was one day showing his line to Mr. Stroke, a drug merchant of a town in the east north southwest. Picking up one of the sample brushes, Mr. S. said to the salesman, 'That's an excellent brush.' Mr. A. answered, 'No, I'm sorry to say it is not. Its bristles fall out easily and the wood is not really rosewood but a cheap imitation.' Mr. S. was so pleased with the young man's candour that he said, 'Mr. A. it is not often I meet a salesman as candid as you are. If you will show me the rest of your line I shall be delighted to fill out a first class order.' 'Mr. S.,' answered Mr. A., 'I'm sorry to say that the whole line is as rotten as that brush.' More delighted than ever Mr. S., who was a widower, invited Mr. A. to his house where he met Mr. S.'s grown-up daughter who kept house for him. The two young people immediately fell in love and were married, Mr. A. moving into the house and taking over the business while Mr. S., now without a home, went out selling brushes."

While we are speaking of the approach of

the prospect it may be well to remind our readers very clearly,—for the poor guys don't seem to get anything unless we make it clear,—that a prospect otherwise invisible may be approached and seen by utilizing his fondness for amusements or sport. Many a man who is adamant at his place of business is mud on a golf course. The sternest and hardest of merchants may turn out to be an enthusiastic angler, or even a fisherman. The salesman who takes care to saunter into the store with a dead catfish in his pocket will meet with a cordial reception; and a conversation pleasantly initiated over the catfish and its habits may end in a handsome order. At other times it is even possible to follow the prospect out to his golf course or to track him out to the trout streams and round him up in the woods. In this case salesmanship takes on a close analogy with out-of-door hunting, the search for the prospect, the stalking of the prospect and the final encounter being very similar to accounts of the stalking of big game.

I append here an illustrative anecdote. As a matter of fact it was written not in reference to salesmanship but as an account of hunting the Wallaboo or Great Hog in the uplands of East Africa. But anybody familiar with stories of salesmanship will see at once that it fits both cases. I have merely altered the wording a little just at the end.

Anecdote of a Hog

"I had been credibly informed," says the writer, "that there was at least a sporting chance of getting in touch with the Great Hog at his drinking time,—"

It will be observed that, apart from the capital letters, this is almost exactly the remark that a salesman often makes.

"The natives of the place told me that the Hog could probably be found soon after daylight at a stream about ten miles away where the brute was accustomed to drink and to catch fish. I, therefore, rose early, rode through the thick squab which covered the upland and reached the stream, or nullah, just after day-break.   There I concealed myself in a thick gob of fuz.

"I had not long to wait.   The Great Hog soon appeared sniffing the air and snorting at the prospect of a drink.   Extending himself prone on the bank with his snout in the water and his huge hind-quarters in the air, the Hog presented an ideal mark for the sportsman.   I rose from my thicket, rifle in hand, and said, 'Mr. A. I have followed you out to this trout stream in the hope of getting a chance to show you my line.   If you have a few minutes at your disposal I shall be glad to show you some samples.   If you don't care to buy anything, I can assure you that it will be a pleasure to show my line.' "

The text seems to go a little wrong here but we can make it all right by reverting to the original which says,—

"After letting him have it thus I had no trouble in hauling the Great Hog up the bank, where I skinned him."

Just one other question may be mentioned before we pass on from this fascinating topic of salesmanship. Should a salesman accept presents, especially presents from ladies? On the whole we think not. It is a delicate problem and one which every young salesman must think out for himself. But the salesman should always remember that a firm refusal if made in a gracious and winning manner is not calculated to give offence. If after concluding his business the salesman finds that the merchant endeavours to slip a bracelet or a pair of earrings into his hand, the salesman should say, "I can't take it, old top, I really can't," then kiss the merchant on the forehead and withdraw.

A present from a lady should be returned with a neat little note so framed as to avoid all offence and yet letting the donor realize clearly that the salesman is not that kind of man.

Let us turn now from the problem of salesmanship to the equally important field of advertising.

The Whole Art of Advertising

I suppose it is no exaggeration to say that salesmanship and advertising are the two most important things in the world. One of the biggest advertising men in the country is reported as saying the other day in his big way, "Where would the world be without advertising?" The more you think of this expression (which only a big man could have expressed) the more you are struck with the truth of it. Indeed it has just exactly that pith, that pep, that punch, which all good advertising ought to have. It sets you wondering right away as to what advertising really is, as to what constitutes good and bad advertising and how the world got on during the dull centuries which did not advertise.

As a matter of fact the world got on very badly. This may be understood when we realize what the world was like before advertising existed. Christopher Columbus, we are told, spent eighteen years vainly trying to persuade the sovereigns of Europe to discover America. Under present conditions all he would have needed to do would have been to circulate among the Kings a form letter with the heading *DO YOU WANT A CONTINENT?* or put a picture of himself on the paper with one hand extended towards a cloud in the sky and the legend *This Man Discovers Continents:* or better still, put up picture placards showing the American Marines at Target Practice in the Matamoras Bay, Mexico.

In other words, advertising has now been reduced to a science, thus taking its place alongside chemistry, salesmanship, dynamics, comparative religion, nursing, astronomy, poultry and other college subjects. It has become the subject of so many manuals and guide books that nothing is easier than to give a brief résumé of the general principles of advertising.

Advertising may be described as the science of arresting the human intelligence long enough to get money from it. It is carried on by means of printed notices, signboards, placards and above all, owing to the simplicity of the human mind, by pictures. It consists of commands, exhortations, adjurations, summonses, directions, and other authoritative appeals. The first essential of a good advertisement or notice is that it must be brief. In the earlier days of advertising this was not understood. When first the railways were built in England and signs were put up to indicate dangerous crossings they were written in small writing and read as follows:—

"Any person or persons proposing to cross this railway track at this point at a time when a train or trains may be approaching is or are warned that if he or she does it, he or they are in danger of coming into collision with it or them."

This was found ineffective. In America the simpler plan was adopted of putting up a notice:—

LOOK OUT FOR THE CARS

Even this was presently found to be too long and was replaced by a simple sign *LOOK OUT*. And perhaps *LOOK* would be enough.

Next to brevity the thing demanded in a

good advertisement is that it should be as per-
emptory as possible.   Fifty years ago such notices were to be seen as the following:—

"No person or persons can be permitted to enter
these premises unless he or it enters in the course of
some definite transaction pertaining to the business of
the company."

This was presently replaced by the sign *"No
admission except on business."*   But how much
superior is the up-to-date printed notice *KEEP
OUT*.

This shows us that every good advertisement must be as personal as possible.   It
should begin *This is You!* or *Listen, you poor
Simp*.   Or it should ask some direct question
such as:—*Do you ever take a Bath!   What
would you do if your wife ran away!* and so
forth.

When once the general principles of advertising language are grasped it is not difficult to
convert ordinary common English into first
class advertising prose.   I will give you a few
examples which will show at once the enor-

mous gain in emphasis, force and directness which is imparted to a passage in literature when it is turned into advertising. Take first a few stanzas from Longfellow written, presumably, with a view to stir the reader into noble activity, but unfortunately expressed in a tone that verges on drowsiness.

"Tell me not in mournful numbers
    Life is but an empty dream,
    For the soul is dead that slumbers,
    And things are not what they seem.

"Life is real, life is earnest,
    And the grave is not its goal.
    Dust thou art, to dust returnest,
    Was not spoken of the soul.

"Let us, then, be up and doing,
    With a heart for any fate,
    Still achieving, still pursuing,
    Learn to labour and to wait."

In a way this is not half bad. There is a certain life to it. But it fails to bring up the idea of the need for immediate effort with sufficient prominence. Compare the advertising counterpart:—

YOUNG MAN, *This is You! Do you want to remain all your life on a low salary! If not why not be up and doing! Still achieving, still pursuing!* We can show you how. *Why not take a correspondence course! Our curriculum includes engineering, poultry, mind reading, oratory, cost accounting and religion. Don't wait. Start achieving now!*

Or take another example from the same poet, the opening lines, I believe, of the poem called "Evangeline."

"This is the forest primeval, the murmuring pines and
    the hemlocks
Stand like Druids of old with beards that rest on
    their bosoms. . . ."

This poem, which was not without merit in its original form, is now immensely improved when used as material for the tourists advertisements.

MR. BUSINESS MAN! *Do you ever take a vacation? What about the Annapolis Valley*

*for the year's outing? Why not visit the
"forest primeval" where you may stand buried
in reverie under the "murmuring pines and
the hemlocks" or emerging enjoy as fine a meal
for a dollar as you will get anywhere. Why
not dream yourself back into the days of the
coureurs des bois and the belted and plumed
seigneurs within easy reach of a garage and
with first class plumbing all through the house.
Why not bring along the wife and take her
into the heart of the primeval forest."*

The next example is taken from Shakespeare.
Originally it formed part of Hamlet's soliloquy
on death, but nearly every line of this passage
has been transposed and improved by the modern advertiser.

> "To be or not to be, that is the question.
> Whether 'tis nobler in the mind to suffer
> The slings and arrows of outrageous fortune
> Or to take arms against a sea of troubles
> And by opposing end them!"

The advertiser expresses the same thought
with much greater point.

The Perfect Salesman

Do you feel only Half Alive? *Are you aware of a heavy sensation after eating and a sense of inflation after drinking a cup of tea! If so, why not "take arms against a sea of troubles."* *Do you know that* Calcul, *taken as one pill a day, will restore tone and vigour to the system, effecting an immediate restoration of the tissues and rebuilding the bones.* *Remember the name,* Calcul!

My readers will long since have suspected,— if the poor simps are sharp enough ever to suspect anything,—that advertising, as we have been seeing again and again, is superior to reality. And this is indeed the case. By the time the advertiser has finished with his exhortations and his glowing descriptions and his pictures he has created a world far brighter than the poor place in which we live.

Who would not wish to be transported to the bright glad world of the painted advertisement and there live forever; there to watch the glistening limousine roll on its distended tires (guaranteed for 20,000 miles) in front of the Georgian residence the shingles of which can be laid by two men in one morning and are really cheaper than the best Italian tiles. See the faultless youth (whose suit, please note it, is marked down to $29.50 but will only stay down till Saturday—you can't *keep* a suit like that down). Watch him as he stands on the clipped green lawn. (The seed of that lawn, can you believe it?, is actually sold for only 50 cents a packet and you can have some.) Observe the gladsome girl beside him. Don't you wish you knew her? Do you know why she is gladsome? It is because her digestion is kept in such extraordinary order by taking one *Calcul* pill a day. I suppose that you are aware that those glistening brown leather shoes that she wears combine style, elegance and comfort in a way that gives ease to the foot and allows free play to the bones of the thorax: if you don't know that you need only consult the little dotted diagram in the corner of the picture showing the human foot anatomically with bones of the thorax moving freely in the fibula: and to think that that shoe can be had *everywhere* at $15.75!

In short, if you will take a comprehensive glance at the red and white house and the green lawn and the glistening motor car and the aspect of young love in the foreground you will realize that advertising is just one more item added to the Pictured Vision of Unreality, better than life itself.

V

ROMANCES OF
BUSINESS

V.—Romances of Business

Note. Business having become the most important thing in life it is quite clear that it is destined to swallow up the feeble things that we used to call literature and art. They must accommodate themselves or die. The two little romances that follow here are intended to show how this accommodation may be effected.

It is now an open secret among all those who have anything to do with the making of the magazines that the advertising pages have come to be more interesting than the rest of the text. They are written by more highly trained and highly paid people, they are better illustrated and carry all through a higher interest, more punch,—in short, any business man turns to the advertising pages first, and only when he has exhausted them does he fall back on the duller pages of romance and fiction which fill up the middle of the magazine. The situation is one which threatens our literature, and I think the time has come when our story writers must create a new interest.

It seems to me that this can best be done by borrowing from the advertising pages the glow of idealization which we have seen them to possess and at the same time that exactness of information as to costumes, materials and prices in which they excel. Out of this a new school of fiction may evolve such stories as:—

No. I

Alfred of the Advertisements

A Romance of the Back Pages

THE earliest recollections of Alfred Ellicott, whose life forms the subject of this chronicle, were of his family home in New England on the banks of the Stickemupabit, a stream noted today for its attraction to tourists, being within easy motor ride from both New York and Boston and reached also by the Boston and Maine Railway, whose admirable dining car service makes access to the district and egress from it a sustained pleasure and which welcomes any complaint from its patrons in regard to the incivility of its employees. Here Alfred passed his boyhood. The house in which he lived was a typical colonial mansion, known in the neighborhood as "The Ads": It was built in the colonial style (See booklet) with a tall portico and wide sloping roof shingled everywhere with the new LAY-EASY shingles, the principal advantage in which is represented by *reducing labour cost,* two men being able easily to lay three squares (30 x 10 ft.) in one morning. In fact these are the shingles of which Mr. P. O. Woodhead (see insert) the well-known builder of Potsdam, New Hampshire, has said in his impressive way *"They reduce cost."*

Here Alfred spent a solitary boyhood, his time spent largely in reverie and day dreams. When not able to sleep naturally he found that two grains of *sleep-tight* inhaled up his nose brought on a delightful slumber from which he awoke completely refreshed at fifty cents a packet.

It was when Alfred had reached the age of
nineteen years that Lovely Louisa, a distant relative, came to live at The Ads. The girl had
been left an orphan, by the death of parents
who had not known that ten minutes' exercise
on the *PRAKTO* System done on the floor of
their bedroom would have preserved the lives
of both of them. She had moreover been rendered penniless by the folly of a guardian who
had never understood that investment is now a
science that can be learned in seven lessons post
paid by applying at once.

Penniless as she was Lovely Louisa on her
arrival at The Ads made an instant impression
on the young and susceptible heart of Alfred.
When she alighted from a motor car the tyres
of which were guaranteed to carry her 20,000
miles and which rolled with excellent softness
over the driveway which had been treated with
ASPHALTOMIX which can be laid on by a
child, the young girl presented a picture that
charmed the eye. She was wearing one of the
new BERSAGLIERI tailored suits which com-

bine smartness with comfort and which have the special advantage that they come in all sizes and can be fitted not only to a frame as slender as Lovely Louisa's but also on ladies of fuller figure. A set of measurements and directions being given with each suit we may be sure that Louisa had such a set with her when she alighted. She wore her suit under one of the new Fascisti hats which kill at a hundred yards and over a pair of tall tan boots which combine grace with comfort by being designed by an expert to fit easily on the instep and to move in harmony with the bones on the anthrax. Under her suit, again,—far under,— Louisa wore one of this year's SKINFIT combinations which was imported directly from Lyons and without which no lady should be. When we say that the girl in alighting made a picture that would have pleased the eye of a hermit or a lobster or an undergraduate, we are not overstating it.

Alfred who was wearing one of the new NOW-OR-NEVER tailored gray suits over brown boots as he stepped forth to meet the girl, felt that his heart was no longer in his own keeping.

During the days which followed the youthful Alfred became the constant companion and, in addition, the guide and mentor of the lovely girl. Himself a keen golfer he had soon initiated his beautiful cousin into the mysteries of golf, and taught her to appreciate a good elastic ball such as the 1924 SMACKO of which the outer case is guaranteed never to chip or crumble. Under the same tutelage the mysteries of MAH JONG, an excellent set of which has now been placed on the market direct from China (remember the words *direct from China*), afforded the young people a fascinating refuge from thought.

It was a great pleasure to Alfred during these sweet hours of companionship to watch the gradual unfolding of the girl's mind. To help it to unfold the young man purchased and read out loud to Louisa a correspondence course in Political Economy and Municipal Taxation, such as would enable the girl to fill a position of trust as tax-assessor, municipal expert, or consulting town engineer. Together also they read over a course on Cost Accounting and Overhead Reckoning by which Louisa would have fitted at any moment to act as an insurance appraiser or to take over bankrupt stock. Then with every day the girl acquired new power of mind and a wider outlook. Indeed as Prof. O. J. Hootch, D.F., organizer of the World's Correspondence School in Room 6 Avenue 4718 Omaha, says: *"Outlook means look out."*

We need not denote in full the blissful but anxious days during which Alfred, conscious of his love, hung suspended between hopes and fears. We will only say that the suspenders that he used were of the new HAUL-OVER type with the central pulley adjusted to the play of his shoulders. No doubt this delicate adjustment helped the young man through the most troubled period of life, keeping his shoulders flat and putting no pressure on his abdomen. In short they are the very braces which Mr. J. O. P. Bughouse of Wichita, Kansas, whose picture is usually annexed, has said— *"They are the only ones I ever use!"*

During this enchanted period of courtship Alfred contrived in various ways to convey the feelings which he dared not utter. Knowing that flowers can now be sent by telegraphic order to any address he had them expressed to Louisa from all parts of the country. These orders which were received at any hour of the day or night were filled under the direction of a staff of trained experts on whose taste and discretion the customer may place the utmost reliance. In short it is of these orders that the well-known florist Mr. J. Q. W. Mud of Wastabula, Wash., has said, in that terse language which he uses *"Let us send them."* In addition to the flowers Alfred also sent seeds, bulbs, and shoots for which the charge is exactly the same and no greater.

The inevitable time drew near when Alfred of The Ads felt that he must know his fate and must hazard all on an avowal of his love. For this however he had prepared himself. He had overcome the natural diffidence of youth by purchasing and perusing a little manual called *Why be Diffident, Self Confidence Acquired By A New System Of Treatment in two lessons at Fifty cents each.* Alfred in sending for this little book enclosed U. S. Postage Stamps but it is important to notice that bills, express orders or any form of legal tender are similarly accepted for it.

Nor was lovely Louisa unprepared. She too had studied a little manual entitled *What a young girl ought to know,* and she knew it.

The fateful moment came. Kneeling on one knee in front of Louisa,—a thing which he was enabled to do without risk by wearing NEVER CREASE trousers,—Alfred declared his love in a few easy sentences selected from his manual. The deep blush which coloured the face of the lovely Louisa was answer enough. Alfred rose to his feet with an easy movement of his suspenders and clasped the girl to his heart.

There is no need here to describe the charming home wedding with which the marriage of

143

Alfred and Louisa was celebrated at The Ads. The good old place was cleaned and redecorated from cellar to basement, Alfred using for this purpose the new PNEUMO-WHEEZE Vacuum Cleaner, which can be had on free trial for ten days and which is *guaranteed* to remove dust from every corner and crevice. It is of this cleaner that Mr. X. Q. Overhead, himself a T. Q. of Yale, the well-known expert has said *"They are the Best Cleaner That I Know."*

The catering was placed in the hands of a catering firm. The invitations were printed and issued by an invitation firm. The officiating clergyman was engaged on a simple basis of cost plus. Louisa looked charming in a wedding gown which could have been returned without charge if not satisfactory. Alfred's costume was guaranteed by the maker himself. And as the happy pair sank back luxuriously on the seat of the landau (a shock absorber with every car) Alfred placed his arm twice round Louisa's waist and murmured, *"It pays to Advertise."*

No. II

Tom Lachford Promoter

A Story which carries with it what is called an Atmosphere of Business and which may safely be read without loss of efficiency.

In the little factory town of Smudgeville the five o'clock whistles blew. The machines stopped. The steam died. The hands quit. The doors closed. The factories shut. Work was over.

Seth Lachford shut the door of the tumble-down place that was called Lachford's Works, and went and sat on a pile of shingles, thinking of his overhead costs. The Lachford business was so undermined by overhead that with any further depression it would go up altogether.

All around Seth as he sat were the great piles of crumbled gray dust that represented his five years' efforts to make cement. The old Lachford farm on the outskirts of the factory town had been all torn up and scarred with the fruitless attempt.

145

As Seth sat there, one might have looked twice, or even three times, at the man without noticing anything especial about him. But if one looked four times one observed more than one has remarked in three times. The face and the attitude were those of a man who had failed. But there was something, too, in the hard-bitten, tight-lipped, close-nipped, short-necked appearance of the man that showed that in his case failure, after all, meant little more than lack of success.

Seth Lachford rose, painfully, from the bunch of shingles, locked the door of the mean place that he called his Works, and walked across the lot to the house he called his home, where the woman he called his wife was cooking supper for the things he called his children.

"Things any better today?" she queried.

Seth head-shook dejectedly.

"Are your overhead expenses per unit of output still disproportionate to the selling cost of the product?" asked the sad-eyed woman as she helped her husband to the fried potatoes.

"Yes, Min," desponded Seth, "The capital cost of operation shows an ascending curve right along."

"I see," said Min, thoughtfully, as she poured out molasses for the children, "and each further increment of outlay merely agglomerates your differential."

"It does," said Seth.

There was a silence and Seth rose.

"Where y' going?" throbbed his wife.

"Out to sit on the shingles," Seth glumped, "and think about my overhead and my differential cost."

"All right," said Min; then, suddenly, her face sanguinated, "Oh Seth," she said, "I forgot, there's a letter from brother Tom. He'll be here in the morning, and he says he can straighten everything out."

II

Next morning Tom Lachford, promoter, blew into Smudgeville, and together Tom and Seth walked round the "plant" and looked at the crumbling piles of gray dust.

The brothers were a contrast—Seth bent and hesitant, Tom square-built, bull-chested, ox-necked, box-jawed, pop-eyed, in short, a hundred and fifty per cent American all through.

"See here, Seth," said Tom, "you've tried five years to make cement and you've failed?"

Seth desponded assent.

"You've crushed up all the rocks on the old place, and you've nothing for it but these piles of dirt."

Seth ingurgitated but without speaking.

"Well, look here," Tom went on, "I've got an idea and it's a big thing. If we can pull it off and bring it down, I believe we can put it over."

"What y' going to do?" asked Seth.

"Going to make a fortune out of this dirt. But, first of all, I want a thousand dollars cash."

"I haven't got it," exhaled Seth, "and the bank won't lend it. I've tried them."

"Pshaw!" said Tom, "show me the way to that bank. I'll get it."

148

Tom Lachford walked straight to the Smudgeville First National Bank, straight into it, and straight through it to the manager's room. There was something compelling about the man, something dynamic in the way he sat down, and something almost titanic or teutonic in the way he laid his hat on the table.

"See here, Mr. Beanhead," he said. "I want the loan of a thousand dollars."

The manager spasmed. "On what security?" he winced.

"None," said Lachford.

The manager brightened.

"You offer no collateral at all?" he said.

"Not a cent," said Tom, "except my personality."

"Good!" said the banker, delighted. "You shall have it. The personal element, Mr. Lachford, has become the ne plus ultra of business. I recognize in you one of those full-blooded, high-pepped, long-sighted, wide-eyed men who are entitled to bank loans. This bank will back you."

III

That night Seth and Min and Tom sat in consultation over their buttermilk and pancakes at the supper table.

"What do you mean to do with the money, Tom?" asked Min.

Tom buttermilked a minute, and then, "Going to get a gang of men and treat that dirt."

"Treat it?"

"Yes, treat it; run it into vats and out again, sluice it, pulverize it, sling it round—anything—"

Seth stopped pancaking and earlifted.

"What's that for?" he exuded.

"I'll tell you," said Tom, "I'm going to raise bonds on it and float a company and make a clean up."

"But it's only dirt!" said Seth, "somehow we failed every time to make it harden into cement."

"I don't want cement," said the promoter.

"Dirt'll do. Here's the idea, I'm going to give it a name—something high-sounding, see! Something that seems to mean value. Did you ever hear of Molybdenum? Well, what is it? You don't know. Or carborundum or tellurium—you don't know what they are. The public don't know what they are. But they mean money. Find a deposit of any of them and your fortune's made."

Seth headnodded silent.

"I'll have an assayer come," Tom went on, "and make an assay of all that dirt and crushed rock. That's only for appearance, of course I don't care what he calls it. I'll give it a name that sounds good and announce it as a big discovery. See? The name I've settled on is palladium. We'll announce a find of palladium, and form a company to work it."

Min looked up from the little pile of children's clothing that she was sewing. "Issuing common stock," she said, as she bit off a piece of thread, "on a basis of prospective earnings capitalized."

151

"But what then?" said Seth. "If we sell the stock and it's no good?"

"We don't need to worry. We sell it and then we clear out."

"Where to?"

The sad-eyed woman looked up from the little garment in her lap.

"Havana," she said.

IV

Within a week it was known all over Smudgeville that heavy deposits of palladium had been found on the old Lachford place. Gangs of men were at work. Derricks, cranes, vats, and sluices rose all over the place. Little crowds of people stood round to watch. The palladium was put into a converter and carried from there to a container from which it passed to a disturber. It was then put into a hopper. "What is it?" asked the people. "Palladium," was the answer. The Smudgeville *Intelligence* explained that palladium was a graminiferous amygdaloid and that its calcareous properties rendered it of great commercial value. It was

152

practically impervious to collusion which made it a high soporific.

An assayer was brought, a real one, and he walked round over the Lachford place and carried off samples. The promoter let all the town know that the assayer had been on the property. But the report of the analysis of the dirt Tom Lachford showed to no one. He shoved it into the drawer of the kitchen dresser unopened. It was the assayer he wanted, not the report.

Then Tom Lachford called again upon the banker.

"Mr. Beanhead," he said, "my brother and I have made a find of igniferous palladium. It runs at least 48 per cent to the kilowatt and we want to raise money for incorporation and material."

"Mr. Lachford," said the banker, "I congratulate you on your discovery. I recognize in you one of those wide-visioned, broad-sighted, frog-eyed men that make this country what it is. How much money do you want?"

"Ten thousand dollars," said Tom.

v

That evening when Tom came home he told Seth and Min that he had arranged the incorporation at thirty thousand dollars and was going to order ten thousand dollars' worth of machinery.

"What machinery?" asked his brother.

"Any machinery," said the promoter, "it doesn't matter: as long as it's bulky."

"The mere assemblage and erection of machinery," added Min thoughtfully as she helped the brothers to fried eggplant, "conveys to the investor a guarantee of bona fides."

But after supper Seth Lachford went to the kitchen dresser and took out of it the assayer's report upon the dirt, that lay in an envelope unopened. He ripped open the envelope and for a long while stood looking at the document with a frown upon his face. "I'll not sell stuff like that," he muttered. "No, sir, I'll go broke before I'll sell it." Then he went out in the gathering dusk and walked among the

154

piles of dirt, kicking it with his feet and picking it up in his hands.

When Seth Lachford came back to the kitchen where Tom and Min sat shucking butternuts there was resolution in his face.

"Tom," he said, "when you sell out this company what do you expect to get?"

Tom looked up, stopped shucking. "Thirty thousand dollars at par," he said. "Ten thousand each for you and me and Min: perhaps a lot more."

"You'll sell it to people here in town?"

"Easy," said Tom. "There are enough suckers right here to buy it all."

"And what do they get?"

"That's their lookout," shrugged Tom. "They can sell again if they're quick enough."

"But sooner or later?"

"Oh, sooner or later someone gets stung. But it's not going to be us."

Seth sat silent a while.

"And if we let go of it now," he asked, "where are we?"

155

"We owe the bank $15,000, and we're ruined."

Seth looked Tom right in the face. Dynamic as he was, the younger Lachford's face fell.

"See here, Tom," evolved Seth slowly, "I'll not sell those shares."

The brothers sat looking at each other, their faces working.

"If you don't," said Tom, "it's ruin."

"I'll meet it," said Seth, his face still working.

"If you do," said Tom, his face stopping working, "you'll meet it in the penitentiary."

"Tom," said Seth, "there's been Lachfords on this place for four generations, and never a thief among them."

VI

For two weeks after that the work at the palladium deposits went on, and the Lachfords walked around the plant, avoiding each other —Tom keen and restless, Seth moody, his eyes ever on the dirt.

Only once Tom spoke to Seth. "The brokers have placed the first lot of my shares at par," he said, "and they can sell more, they say. They can't list them but they'll sell them on the curb. Give me your shares now and Min's and we'll sell them and get out."

Seth turned on his heel and, without a word, went to the house.

He called his wife aside. He took out the assayer's paper, opened it, and spread it out before her. "Tom says he'll sell your shares for ten thousand dollars, Min. Are you going to sell off that stuff," and he tapped the paper fiercely, "to your friends and neighbors, people of your own town?"

Min looked at the document. The chemical analysis was beyond her grasp, but the single item at the bottom, "estimated commercial value," was plain enough even for a child.

"No, Seth!" she said, "I can't do it. It ain't right."

"Look, Min," Seth went on, "I want my name to stand right in this town. If Tom tries to sell out those shares, could you get ten thousand dollars from your folks and buy them?"

"I might," said Min, "I doubt Pa could raise it, but if you want it, Seth, I'll try."

VII

The next day Min started off to her folks in Pennsylvania to raise ten thousand dollars, and on the same morning the shares of Amalgamated Palladium Limited went on the local exchange as a curb security, and there was great excitement in financial circles in Smudgeville. The shares opened at eighty, rose straight to par, reacted to fifty, sank down to twenty, lay there gasping and then jumped to par again in four hops. At 2 P. M. they were reported as restless; at 3 buoyant, and at closing time strong with an undercurrent of weakness.

That night Tom Lachford packed his grip to leave by the midnight express, bound towards Havana.

"I'm off, Seth," he said; "say goodby to Min when she comes back. If you're wise you'll get quick. The shares will break tomorrow and then—"

"I'm not quitting, Tom," said Seth; "goodby."

VIII

Min came back two days later.

"I got the money, Seth," she said. "Pa raised it partly on the steers and the rest on a mortgage."

"Too late, I guess, Min," said Seth. "The shares went to five hundred yesterday, and this morning they're holding out for a thousand dollars a share."

IX

It was a week later that Tom Lachford sat in the Colorado Claro Hotel at Havana with a cocktail in front of him, and $4,000 in Cuban money to his credit. And it was there he got a copy of a home paper sent him by mail. He opened it with trembling hands, looking for Seth's ruin. And instead of it he saw a big headline saying that Amalgamated Palladium was selling at two thousand a share, and his hands trembled more. Last of all he read a two-column account of the discovery of graphite on the Lachford place, and he shook like a leaf all over.

Meantime Min and Seth were sitting over their buttermilk in the kitchen living-room, adding up figures.

"I can't cipher it out," said Seth, "but it's millions all right."

"And what is the stuff anyways," asked Min, "if it ain't palladium?"

"Graphite, it's called," said Seth. "Always noticed those black streaks in the crushings. I guess that's it. I'm glad I didn't sell. If I could have bought back those shares I meant to give them to Tom, didn't I, Min?"

"Oh, certainly," said Min, "so did I: and I'm glad too we didn't sell. I felt bad about it all along, Seth, and when I saw that assayer's paper where it said 'commercial value ten thousand dollars a ton' a light broke in on me and I saw it wasn't right. But I still don't see why those shares jumped up that way."

"The damn fool assayer. He must have put some New York guys wise to it. They were just waiting for us, likely. I doubt, Min, whether those New York financiers are quite as easy as they make out in the story papers."

"That's so," subsided Min. "And where Tom was a bum promoter, Seth was wrong in underestimating the commercial value of scientific analysis applied to the basic data of modern business."

No. III

Our Business Benefactors

An After-Dinner Symposium, as Reported by the Humblest of the Guests

"No," said Mr. Spugg, the host of the party, as he held one hand on the stem of his port wine glass and kept his second after-dinner cigar in the fingers of the other, "no Sir, I never could do fractions."

He looked round the table with a sort of pride. All the other men, except myself, grunted assent. "And what's more," added Spugg, "I've never felt the need of them to this day." There was a chorus of approval. Spugg of course is a *big* man, one of the biggest men in rubber, so they say, on the continent. There were other big men present at the dinner too. There was a big shirt man, and a big fruit man and a man at the end of the table that I had frequently heard referred to as the Napoleon of frozen meat. In fact, as has been indicated in earlier pages of this book, in such a gathering as this there were certain to be several *Napoleons* present,—who were spoken of as "regular Napoleons," "perfect Napoleons" and so on. They are always found in any business gathering. There were some "revolutionists" present also; one man was pointed out to me as having revolutionized the dried apple business: another had revolutionized the sale of weatherproof paint, and a third was "working up a revolution" in eggs. In short they were a typical group of what are now called "big" men—men who do "big" things. They were not "thinkers." They were men who don't need to think. So it is naturally most impressive to hear these men say that they had never done fractions in their lives. If big men like them have no use for

fractions what earthly good are fractions anyway? But what interested me most was to
hear the "big men" talk of the "side lines," the
things that they carried on as mere appendages
to the main interests of their business lives.

"How's that University of yours getting on,
Spugg?" asked the big pulp man. "Better,"
said Spugg, "We've got a business man at the
head of it at last and he's putting it on business
lines. We expect that our next balance sheet
will make a pretty good showing."

"That's good," said the other. Then they
both fell silent to listen to the Napoleon of
frozen meat who was talking, so I gathered
presently, about the church that he "controlled."

"He had," the Napoleon was saying "no pep,
no punch. Sunday after Sunday it was the
same thing,—every sermon, you know, just so
much straight Theology. Well, you see, a
congregation won't stand for Theology today.
They want something up-to-date. Two or
three times I got hold of the old fellow and I
said to him, 'can't you take up something that

will let the people get away a little further from religion.' But he couldn't. It wasn't in him."

"Couldn't you retire him?" asked one of the listeners.

"Not so very easily. We had no written contract, you know, just the old fashioned appointment by letter—(it was forty years ago when they put him in) and all the original letter said, was, 'as long as it shall please God to bless his ministration,'—Well, I began to say what can you do with that? Our lawyers admitted that they couldn't make sense of it.

"Then there was all the trouble about the churchyard,"—went on the big man, pausing to light a new cigar. "You remember that churchyard that there was all round our church with the willow trees and the gravestone and the old slabs laid flat right in the grass?"

Several men nodded.

"Well you know, that sort of thing is a pretty poor ad. for a church. The stones were old, half crumbling and there wasn't a willow tree in the lot in decent shape. Of course we

wanted to level it all out, clean out the old mon-
uments, cut out the trees and turf it neatly, put
a good gravel motor drive in a crescent right
through it.   Well, the old fellow stood out
against it and without his consent, so our lawyers said, we ran a certain risk in removing the
dead.   There is some old law it seems against
'breaking the repose of the dead.'   It has no
application I understand to an up-to-date cem-
etery.   But it applies here.   So we were stuck.
Meantime the churchyard was doing us harm:
a congregation don't want to drive their cars
among graves over grass.   The broken stone
will blow a tire as quick as anything."

"Well, what did you do?" asked Spugg,
"Oh we got him out all right," the big man
went on.   "We managed to get him in a corner on the pension question and he let us have
his resignation."   "And who have you got
now?"   "We've got an A. 1 man, all right.
He was with the Presbyterians (though I think
he'd been an Anglican for a while before that)
but we went straight after him, met him at his
own figure and signed him."

"What are you giving him?" asked Spugg. "Fifteen Thousand," said the Napoleon, puffing at his cigar. "You can't get them for less, or not good ones. They simply won't come: They know what they're worth. There's an insurance company that would take our man at fifteen thousand tomorrow."

"He's pretty good, is he?" asked one of the men.

"Absolutely first class. He's the best publicity man I ever saw in a pulpit. You've seen that big sign he's put up, with great gilt letters, —just where the old willow with the sundial under it used to be. Every week there's the topic of the discourse in big lettering so that people can read it from their cars: and *those* are the people, mind you, that we're going after. Under the old fellow we had, I suppose, the poorest congregation in the city. A church can't get very far with *them*."

There was a general growl of agreement.

"And every Sunday some new up-to-date subject, not theology you know but something that will hold and interest the people. Last Sun-

166

day, for example, he preached on the Holy Land (he was there for the Standard Oil people six or seven years ago). And he showed it all so vividly (we've fixed a moving picture machine where the font used to be), with the borings that they're making for oil near Damascus, and the new derricks at the Sea of Galilee. It was wonderful."

"But that's a pretty heavy sum to pay him," one of the guests said, "I don't see how your funds can meet that."

"Just the other way," said the big man, "we make on it. With a live man like that you get it all back. Last Sabbath day our offertory alone broke even with the week's expenses: that will show you the class of people that we're attracting."

"That's certainly pretty good," assented several of the men.

"Yes and more than that. Take the overhead. Now, in the old fashioned church the overhead was everything. Light and power alone were among the biggest items that they thought about. Well, we've changed all that.

167

You can't exactly cut out the overhead altogether in running a church, but you can reduce it to a point where it doesn't matter. And what we find is that with plenty of current receipts from Social entertainments,—concerts and lotteries and dances and so on, we don't have to worry about the questions of light and power at all. In fact we never think of it."

The speaker paused. And the host took occasion of the pause to start the port wine moving round and to beckon to the butler for more cigars. Whereupon the general talk broke out again and the purely spiritual tone of the conversation was lost.

But I couldn't help revolving in mind as I presently wended my way home, the wonderful things that the Big Business men are doing for our Colleges and Churches.

VI.
THE PERFECT LOVER'S GUIDE

VI.—The Perfect Lover's Guide

Or

How to Select a Mate, on Sea or on Shore

Our progress through the Garden of Folly having led us to view the follies of the mind and body, of failure and success, we are now brought in sight of the supremest folly of all, the most ancient and the most modern, the folly of love. We suppose that even the dullest of our readers—and we are speaking with emphasis—will sit up here and give evidence of something approaching to an intelligent interest. Indeed we may say that we have been induced to make up this part of our enquiry in response to a wide public demand,—the only reason, by the way, which induces us to do anything. We therefore propose to construct in condensed form a sort of Lover's Guide or Manual of Love.

Preface

On the Importance of Selecting a Wife

FEW people appreciate at its true importance the selection of a wife. One has only to look at other men's wives to realize how carelessly they have been selected. A great many of them are too small, others are too large. Others again, while suitable as to size are of poor quality. With others the colouring is imperfect, or easily washed out. In short if a man desires to select a wife of the right size and shape, of good colour and wearing quality, one that is washable and will not bleach out in the sun, he must be willing to devote time and study to the question. Many a young man admits after marriage with regret that he has selected his wife too rashly: that if he had used an intelligence test on her he would never have taken her: that he thought she knew things that she doesn't know: that her sense of humour is away below his standard: that she can't play poker,—and that he would like another pick.

For such young men there is no hope to be given. Their choice is made. But those whose selection is still to be taken we would advise to be warned in time and to study the whole problem of selecting a wife with the care that it deserves.

At What Age Should a Man Marry

Our first enquiry, then, is the age at which a man ought to turn his thoughts towards marriage? The law of the State of New York, and of many other states, and the common law of England on which these laws are based, all assign as the age of marriage fourteen years for a man and twelve years for a woman. But we are against this. We have a feeling that it is too soon. A man of fourteen still lacks something in breadth,—and even in height. We doubt if his character has reached the maturity that it will have at sixty. Similarly a woman of twelve is still in a way,—indeed in a whole lot of ways—undeveloped, she has scarcely seen enough of life to be able to select a mate with the same certainty with which the shipping companies pick them. We are informed, it is true, that the Hindoo women are married at twelve years of age. But on this point we can only refer our readers to the Hindoo edition of our manual. Western women, at twelve, are not yet formed. The wise young man will wait until they get bigger. Anyone who wants one of those little wee Hindoos is welcome to her.

At what age, then, should a young girl or a young man begin to think of marriage? We are not prepared to indicate any precise moment in life. But there will come a time in the life of any of them at which new aspirations and new wants will turn their thoughts towards marriage. When a young girl begins to feel that she wants a house of her own,—a large one,—with a butler and a chauffeur, and two motor cars and a box at the Opera, then the time has come when she must seek a husband. Her father will never give her these things.

174

So too with the young man. The time comes when his surroundings begin to pall on him— when he ceases to care to spend his evenings with billiard markers, prize fighters and dog fanciers: when he begins to want to pass his time with some companion softer than a prize fighter and dearer,—if it is possible,—than a dog fancier,—then, we say, and we say it emphatically, the young man ought to get married.

What Young People Ought to Know

But stop! Before the young man, or the young woman, can take any steps in the direction of marriage they must first fit themselves for it. All the manuals on the subject are united on this. Young people must not be hurried into matrimony until they have an adequate knowledge of a great many things that it will be essential for them to know in married life. Most important is it that our young people should have a proper acquaintance with the laws of health, a knowledge in short, of their own bodies. The young men and women of our present generation,—in spite of the existence of the admirable little manuals of Dr. Snide, Dr. Snoop and others,—are painfully ignorant of their own bodies. We ourselves met a girl the other day,—a great big one, not a little Hindoo,—who didn't know where her œsophagus was. Apparently she had been going round with her œsophagus for twenty years and didn't know that she had one. Enquiry showed that she was also ignorant of her diaphragm and what it did for her, and knew nothing of her cerebellum except that it was part of her foot.

This girl, charming as she appeared externally,—we went no further than that,—was obviously unfitted for matrimony. Indeed we should strongly advise every young lover to see to it that no girl, suffering from ignorance of this sort, is wished upon him. The lover should first elicit by a little gentle questioning just what is the state of knowledge of his prospective bride. He may frame his questions with a tenderness calculated to allay any possible alarm: such as:—"Whisper to me, darling, what do you take to be the primary functions of the liver? or, "Tell me, dearest, what are the premonitory symptons of coagulation of the head?"

If the anxious lover does not feel in himself the ability to elicit or to impart this knowledge without help he may very properly call to his aid the services of an examination paper as set in any medical college. In this he need only insert a few suitable terms of endearment and the aim is achieved at once. His questionnaire, for example, might take this form:—

1. Indicate as briefly as possible, darling, the location and functions of the sebaceous glands.

2. Tell me, in your own bright way, the names of the bones of the head, and then give me a kiss.

3. What do you take to be the premonitory symptoms, sweetheart, of locomotor ataxia and what would my darling do if I got it?

But it would be greatly to be preferred that no such test would be necessary. We should advise for every young girl who is thinking of marriage a proper course of preparation. We would suggest that she read first of all *Gray's*

Anatomy, supplementing it with *Archibald on the Diseases of the Bones:* to this she might add *Adami on Pathology, Todd on Parasitology* and any standard text on locomotor ataxia. If in addition to this the girl has learned something of sanitation, of the elements of sewerage and the disposal of garbage, she then becomes one with whom any young man should be proud to share his home,—especially the cellar and the plumbing.

Nor should the youth himself be ignorant. His body of course he must know from A to Z. He should be able to tell offhand, how many toes he has, the location of his ears, the number of vertebræ in his spine, the measurement of his facial angle, the spanal content of his skull and the width of his mouth. These things go without saying. But in addition to this no young man should hurry into marriage without some acquaintance with the world and especially with business and money. We met a young man the other day,—we are always meeting them when we least expect it,—hoping to get married shortly and yet absolutely ignorant of the Federal Reserve system, and the composition of Index Numbers and the rise and fall of the exchanges. We at once put in his hands Gustav Kassel's *Arithmetic of the Exchanges* and Professor J. M. Keynes's *Incubation of a Monetary Standard*. We were just in time. He decided not to get married.

Courtship, its Conduct and its Etiquette

But let us suppose these preliminary difficulties overcome. Imagine our young people as having reached the age of marriage and properly equipped with the necessary knowledge for the marriage state. What Next?

There follows then the period of love and courtship, admittedly the most blissful phase of human existence. The young lover though he has selected his mate has not yet ventured to declare himself. He is filled with hopes and fears, with alternating exaltation and despair. At one moment he is in the heights: at another he is in the depths. He goes away up and then away down. He oscillates to and fro, at one instant he is hurled forward, at another he is shot backward. At times again he is whirled sideways and thrown edgeways or left sticking wrong side up. How must the lover conduct himself during this period of violent emotion? How must his time be spent? What can he do to absorb the terrific shocks which come at him one after the other?

We have no hesitation in answering this enquiry. All the authorities on the subject are agreed upon the point. The young lover must spend his time in immediate communion with nature. Fleeing the crowded haunts of man he must go and bury himself in the forest; there in the heart of the woods he must lie prone upon his back looking upwards at the sky and thinking what a worm he is. Or he must climb to the height of the mountains and stand upon a dizzy crag letting the wind blow through his hair. While doing this he must reflect how little it would matter if the wind blew him into fragments and carried him away. In all weathers he must sally forth. He must let the storm buffet him. He must let the rain beat upon his brow. He must take crack after crack of lightning right on his neck.

Just why he must do these things we are not prepared to say. But we *know* that only in this way can the lover get himself into that attitude of humility and ecstasy which can make him worthy of his adored.

This course of conduct having been admitted, by generations of poets and lovers, to be absolutely compulsory, we venture in our manual to simplify it a little by reducing it to a routine. In this way the young lover who might have had some doubts as to where and how to begin can undertake his duties in a systematic way.

Schedule of the Perfect Lover's Day

5.30 Dawn	Rise from a sleepless night.
6.00	Lave himself in a running brook, or if this is not possible, put his head under a tap.
6.30-7.30	Crag work on the hills.
8.00	Push aside his untasted breakfast.
8.30-12.00	Lie on stomach in long grass in meadow, poring on a book.
12 Noon	Returning for a moment to busy haunt

of man or crowded mart (that is to say, going down town) catch sight, on the street for a moment, of adored object, and at once

12.30   beat it for the woods

12.30 till dark:

in the woods; alone with nature: penetrating to the heart of the woods, go and sit in frog pond, making a sound like a frog.

8.30-9.30   For one brief hour be with adored object: the outside world will see him nothing but a gentleman friend taking a lady friend for a ride on a street car: but really the buffeting and the oscillating and side-swinging is going on all the time just the same.

10 P. M.   A dash for the open. Get out under the stars. Count them. Wonder whether they are looking down on her also.

12 Midnight   Retire to sleepless night but before starting it, throw the casement wide and let the cool night wind slap the face.

We not only assert but we are willing to *guarantee* that this line of activity, systematically kept up for a month, will maintain the lover in the condition proper to his business. He will be brought nearer and nearer to the point at which he will stake his all on a proposal of marriage.

But meantime before we permit him to take this last step it is proper to consider the conduct of the object of his affections. What is she doing? How does she take it? Is she swinging back and forward and up and down and being impelled sideways in the same way as the young lover? Not quite.

For the young girl the first dawn of love is a period of doubt, of hesitating, of gentle fluttering to and fro. She needs guidance. Like a dove about to spread its wings on a far flight, she would fain ask herself whither this flight must lead. What sort of a flight is it going to be?

Nor is she willing to confess to herself that love has yet come to her? She does not know whether what she feels is love, or is something else. Her soul shrinks from the final avowal.

In this position, the girl needs beyond everything else, advice.   And fortunately for her she can get it.   In earlier times she was left to commune with her soul in the dark.   Now she isn't. All she has to do is to write to any reputable Saturday afternoon edition of a first-class paper and she can get advice and information suited to every stage of her incipient courtship. Each letter in which her timid soul reveals itself will be not only answered, but answered in print in a way calculated to gratify her whole circle of friends.

We need hardly say, therefore, that in preparing our manual we have devoted very especially attention to correspondence of this sort. We have endeavoured to reduce it like everything else to a systematic or general form, to make it as it were a type or pattern, from which the young girl seeking our aid (and we welcome her with open arms when she does it) may find complete guidance.

We append here one little series from the many samples of correspondence that might be offered.   The details vary but the essential ideas are always the same.   And we draw at-

184

tention especially to the way in which the tender hesitating nature of the young girl is brought, under our guidance, to a full knowledge of herself. In fact, what we couldn't teach her isn't worth knowing.

The Tangled Problems of Love

As straightened out in the Correspondence department of our manual

Letter No. 1 From our correspondent, Miss Lucinda Lovelorn, to ourselves. By the way, we named her. We know how to pick the names every time.

Two days ago I was introduced by a gentleman friend to a gentleman in a street car. Yesterday I met this second gentleman on the street and he asked me if I would walk with him afternoons. I do not know yet whether I love him as I have only seen him on a street car. Perhaps you can tell me whether it would be right for me to walk with him afternoons and whether there would be anything unladylike in my doing so. If I walk with him is it proper to walk on the left side of a gentleman or does the lady walk on the right side.

Letter No. 2   From ourselves to Lucinda

Yes, we think you may safely accept the invitation to walk with your new friend afternoons. Whether you walk on his left side or his right will depend on circumstances. If he has lost his left eye you walk on his right side, otherwise you have your pick of sides.

But remember, Lucinda, that you must let him see from your manner at the very first that your feeling for him is purely one of wholesome camaraderie and nothing further.   Without being cold to him, put into your manner just that little touch of hauteur and that suspicion of eloignement that will let him realize that you are a lady.

In other words we mean don't let him start anything.   Do you get us?

Letter No. 3   From Lucinda to us

The gentleman friend with which I have been walking afternoons asked me if he might call mornings and also take me out nights. I do not know whether I love him yet although he is a good dresser. Will it be all right if I let him take me pictures nights. Till now whenever gentleman friends have taken me places evenings Mother has been along. If I go with this party pictures do you think that I compromise myself and if it was you would you have mother along.

Letter No. 4   From us to Lucinda

We have thought over your sweet letter very deeply, dear Lucinda, because we realize how perplexed and troubled you are. On the whole we think that you may now safely go out at night with your new friend but remember that in granting him this privilege you must let him know that you have in no way ceased to be a lady. It would be necessary for you to resist in a dignified way any undue advances that he may make. We would suggest that you carry a tack hammer along with you and if your new friend starts anything let him have it on the bean. And by the way let us know what he does about the advances. We are always interested in that sort of thing.

We note further, that you ask whether, if it was we, we should want your mother along. No, dear, we wouldn't.

Letter No. 5   From Lucinda to us

Since I wrote you last the gentleman friend of which I spoke took me out twice nights. I do not know whether I love him dearly yet but he is to have an increase of salary from his firm because he is an A. I. salesman. The last time we went out he asked me if I liked lobsters because if I did he knew where they had a good lobster place but I said no because I thought that a party respects a girl more if she refuses lobsters gentlemen. All the time we were out he behaved just like a perfect gentleman and didn't do anything. Do you think that if he asks me again it would be all right to let him give me lobsters nights?

Letter No. 6   From us to Lucinda

We are glad to learn that your evening outing with your friend was so successful. And it is nice to think that he did not make any wrong advances at all, but behaved like a perfect gentleman.

But when it comes to this lobster stuff, you touch on something that we *know* and on which we speak with the greatest firmness. It is not proper for you to accept a lobster unless you have reason to believe that in giving it he is asking you to share his life.

The time has come for you, dear little girl, to be very firm. You must ask your gentleman friend to come home with you to your house and meet your mother. If he is a man, he will do it. But if he shrinks from it and offers you a lobster instead then it is clear that he has been trifling with your heart—and you must let him go. You will suffer a little *mal de cœur* but so you would if you took the lobster. On the other hand if your firmness wins, you gain a husband and a home.

Hence our advice is,—go to it, Lucinda.

After we have carried on and concluded a

correspondence such as this it is always a delight for us to receive a final letter, effervescent in happiness, stating that the proposal has been made and accepted and asking what presents and how many presents a girl may accept from a gentleman to whom she is engaged.

And, what is always a strange reflection to us, is, that this gentleman friend with the lobsters is the very same person as the young lover beating it up and down in the woods:—the same person, only seen in different aspects.

The Proposal of Marriage

But we are running on a little too fast. We have run clear over the proposal of marriage, the most important, the most thrilling item of the whole manual of love.

In what way, we are asking and we ask back, should a proposal of marriage be made. Now we readily admit that the proposal of marriage is most frequently made by direct speech, in short by word of mouth. This may have certain advantages in the way of directness, rapidity and ease of ratification. But we cannot but feel that it lacks much in symmetry, harmony, and all-round completeness. We therefore favour entirely the proposal of marriage by means of a written letter. This allows the lover to state his feelings so definitely and so finally that a refusal becomes difficult if not impossible.

For such a letter, however, it is not wise to rely upon the unaided imagination. Here again the use of a systematized form is greatly to be preferred. The general requirements for such a letter we are prepared to state in the following terms, which are based we may say on some of the greatest current authorities.

"In the perfect letter of proposal the young lover should first of all dwell upon the depth and sincerity of his love. He should express at the same time his esteem and appreciation of the family into which he hopes to have the honour of entering. And in conclusion in a manly and frank way he should say something about his own position in life and his prospects."

On this basis we venture to suggest the following form:

Dear Miss Blank Blank:

Ever since I first had the honour of meeting you beside the sawdust pile behind the sawmill at the Y.M.C.A. picnic on the 18th June, Ult. I have realized that I entertain for you a feeling which is different from any feeling which I have hitherto entertained for anyone for whom I have entertained a feeling. Your coming into my life has brought something into my life which was not in my life before you brought it into my life. I cannot hope in any way to be worthy of you and the more I think of you the more I despise myself and realize that till I met you I had been moving steadily down, but that after I met you I went up and I think that with your help I could keep on going up and staying up. Since I met you I have also had the pleasure of meeting your mother and your father and I have learned to love and honour them. I think your father is too cute for anything. Didn't he look just killing in that little velvet smoking jacket the other evening? My feelings toward your mother are also a matter which I think should give me an added claim to your favourable consideration. I myself never had a mother. But now that I have seen yours I am, in a way, glad.

My prospects in life are such as will at least enable me to maintain you as well as you are maintained now. My salary while not large will suffice to support you and to dress you in part at least which is all I dare ask at present. At my uncle's death I expect to inherit a very comfortable personal fortune and it is clear therefore that in order to be in a satisfactory situation I have only to poison my uncle.

On all these grounds I venture to ask your hand in marriage and to request the favour of a reply at your early convenience to B. 606, Station B.

It is hardly necessary for us to indicate the correct form in which an answer to such a letter of proposal should be framed. The training in business correspondence now given to all young girls in our secondary schools makes such a composition a matter of extreme ease. But we might merely suggest that the normal and usual answer in the best circles runs as follows:

Dear Sir:

Yours of the 18th instant to hand and contents noted and in reply would say that I accept your proposal F.O.B. this city, and will take delivery of goods at any time. Love and kisses from your loving

LUCINDA

The Physiology of Love

While we were discussing above the question of what young people ought to know in regard to their œsophagi and so forth, it occurred to us that we might append to this discussion a further treatment of the physiology of love. We said nothing about it at the moment but we went on thinking about it. The topic sounded daring but that wasn't really the aspect of it that we had in mind. Our notion was, and is, to use it in a literary way for the general brightening of fiction. It seemed to us that modern fiction already owed much to the physiologist and might with advantage go still further in the same direction.

We were first led to think of this from perusing an up-to-date crime-story in which we noticed the following physiological changes to take place in the sleuth hound's face, all in five minutes.

To begin with :—

An impassive mask covered it.

Then, A quick suspicion chased itself across it,

" An intense determination hardened it,

Then, A bead of moisture appeared upon it,
" A smile passed over it,
" A gleam of intelligence shot across it,
" A look of perplexity furrowed it,
" A sudden flash of triumph lighted it up,
And then,
   The impassive mask fell on it again.
These rapid changes of the face are evidently connected with the pursuit of crime. If anybody wants to go in for a life of crime,—on either side, for it or against it,—he has to learn to use his face in this way. He must be able to harden it, relax it, expand it at will and, if need be, to drop a mask right over it,—like putting it into a garage.

But it is quite different, we have observed with the love story, the seat of which seems to be in the stomach. In the same romance in which the sleuth hound worked his face, we noticed that a similar lot of physiological disturbances were set up at intervals in the heroine. In her case, however, the symptoms did not sweep over her face, which was needed for other purposes. They were internal. They began as soon as she met the hero, and anyone will easily recognize in them the progress and the fate of love.

The series ran like this:—

A new gladness ran through her.

.   .   .   .

A thrill coursed through her.

.   .   .   .

Something woke up within her that had been dead.

.   .   .   .

A great yearning welled up within her.

.   .   .   .

Something seemed to go out from her that was not of her nor to her.

.   .   .   .

Everything sank within her.

.   .   .   .

This last symptom is naturally so serious that it ends the book. Indeed we notice that when things sink inside the heroine it means that something vital has come unhooked.

Quite different is the case of the hero,—the strong man. With him the operation of the story is all done seemingly with strings, with stretching and tension. He gets "taut," or he gets "rigid," his muscles "tighten into steel bands,"—in fact you could easily run a sewing machine off him.

Now there is no doubt that these physiological descriptions are admirable in their realism. The only trouble is that they don't go far enough. It has seemed to us that, with the help of a good text book an excellent literary effect could be obtained by heightening this physiological colouring and letting it be quite clear just what is happening, anatomically and biologically, to the characters in the story. To illustrate this we append here a sample of such a romance. The story is called *Physiological Philip* and it tells of nothing more unusual than the meeting of two lovers in a lane. But slight as it is it will do to convey our idea.

Physiological Philip

A Tale of the Text Book

Philip Heatherhead,—whom we designate Physiological Philip—as he strolled down the lane in the glory of early June, presented a splendid picture of young manhood. By this we mean that his bony framework was longer than the average and that instead of walking like an ape he stood erect with his skull balanced on his spinal column in a way rarely excelled even in a museum. The young man appeared in the full glory of perfect health: or shall we say, to be more exact, that his temperature was 98, his respiration normal, his skin entirely free from mange, erysipelas and prickly heat.

As Physiological Philip walked thus down the lane, listening to the singing of a blithesome bird,—occasioned, though he did not suspect it, by a chemical reaction inside the bird's abdomen,—a sense of gladness seemed to fill him. Of course what really was happening was that in the splendid shape in which Philip was his whole system was feeling the stimulus of an intermolecular diffusion of inspired oxygen. That was why he was full.

At a turn of the path Philip suddenly became aware of a young girl advancing to meet him. Her spinal column, though shorter than his,

was elongated and erect, and Philip saw at once
that she was not a chimpanzee. She wore
no hat and the thick capillary growth which
covered her cranium waved in the sunlight and
fell low over her eye-sockets. The elasticity of
her step revealed not the slightest trace of ap-
pendicitis or locomotor ataxia, while all thought
of eczema, measles or spotty discoloration of
the cuticle was precluded by the smoothness and
homogeneity of her skin.

At the sight of Philip the subcutaneous pig-
mentation of the girl's face underwent an inten-
sification. At the same time the beating of the
young man's heart produced in his countenance
also a temporary inflammation due to an under-
oxydization of the tissues of his face.

They met, and their hands instinctively
clasped, by an interadjustment of the bones
known only in mankind and the higher apes
but not seen in the dog.

For a moment the two lovers, for such their
physiological symptoms, though in themselves
not dangerous provided a proper treatment
were applied without delay, proclaimed them,

were unable to find words. This, however, did not indicate (see *Barker on the Nervous System*) an inhibition of the metabolism of the brain but rather a peculiar condition of the mucous membrane of the lip, not in itself serious.

Philip found words first. He naturally would, owing to the fact that in the male, as Darwin first noticed, the control of the nerve ganglions is more rigid than in the female.

"I am so glad you've come," he said. The words were simple (indeed he could hardly have made them simpler unless by inserting the preposition "that" and restoring the auxiliary from its abbreviated form.) But simple as they were, they thrilled the young girl to the heart,—obviously by setting up the form of nerve disturbance which Huxley has so admirably described in his discussion of the effect of external stimuli on the decomposition of food.

"I couldn't stay away," she murmured.

The text is here a little perplexing. No doubt the girl refers to some inhibition in her feet, involving an inability to use the great Toe.

It is an obscure malady and Sir William Osler inclined to ascribe it to excessive alcoholism. But she may have had it. Unfortunately the current of the romance moves on too fast to allow investigation.

Philip reached out and drew the girl towards him.

"Then my answer is Yes," he cried, jubilantly. To do this he inhaled deeply and then ejected the entire contents of his lungs with a sudden impetus. In the dog, this produces barking. (See Sir Michael Foster on Animal Physiology.)

"It is!" she murmured.

Philip drew the girl's form towards him till he had it close to his own form, and parallel to it, both remaining perpendicular, and then bending the upper vertebræ of his spinal column forwards and sideways he introduced his face into a close proximity with hers. In this attitude, difficult to sustain for a prolonged period, he brought his upper and lower lips together, protruded them forward, and placed them softly against hers in a movement seen also in the orang-outang but never in the hippo-potamus.

And with this kiss the affianced lovers wandered back hand in hand up the lane, the bird upon the bough singing more blithely than ever:—owing possibly to the increased disten-tion of its diaphragm.

VII
STUDIES
IN THE PROGRESS OF
HUMAN KNOWLEDGE

VII.—The Restoration of Whiskers A Neglected Factor in the Decline of Knowledge

THERE comes a time in the life of western civilization when it is the duty of every well-wisher of the world to speak out what is in his mind.   Such a time is now. The growth of the clean-shaving habit in this epoch is becoming everywhere a serious national menace.   The loss of dignity and prestige, the decline of respect towards the aged, the notable change in the character and calibre of our legislators, college presidents and ministers of the gospel, is, and are, assuming proportions which urgently demand concerted national action.

The writer of this article stood recently upon the corner of Broadway and Forty Second Street in New York,—that is to say I stood there myself,—let there be no concealment in this thing,

—stood there and counted the clean-shaven men who passed and the men with whiskers. Out of the first half million counted only 4.19 men per cent had whiskers.

(The man that I counted as .19 had just a little fringe of fluff, so to speak, on his cheeks. It was hard to class him. So I called him .19).

The same calculation may be made with the same results in any of the great eastern cities. It is not till one passes a line drawn through Fargo, Omaha, and Galveston that whiskers reach 15 per cent. And this 15 per cent line *is moving westward!* Ten years ago it was at Decatur, Illinois. It is not there now! In another ten years the line will have reached the Rocky Mountains. In twenty years the entire nation will be clean-shaven.

The moment to act is now. It is time for the people to pause and realize what whiskers have meant to human civilization.

We turn to the records of history; Adam,— he had a dark brown beard slightly pointed; Noah,—he had a long white beard that reached his waist. Imagine Noah clean-shaven and with his eyebrows darkened with black dye, and with little beady eyes looking down under a straw hat! You can't? Of course not. And yet that man saved our whole race.

Nestor and Aristotle had white beards. Socrates' whiskers covered so much of his face that you could hardly see him through them. Cæsar had a rough red beard. The Vikings had long side moustaches. So had Buffalo Bill, and Charles the Second, and Bret Harte. Grant and Lee wore beards. But these great precedents are being disregarded. All the dignitaries and leaders of today are fashioning themselves into the likeness of schoolboys.

Take the typical case of the college presidents. A generation ago the college president had a flowing white beard. It was part of his equipment. I remember well the venerable gentleman who was the head of the University when I received my degree thirty something years ago. I shall always recall the profound respect that the students felt towards him. Yet it was not what the man *said:* it was the way in which he laid his snow white whiskers on his reading desk. This lent profundity to all his thought. It was, I think, in the year 1892 that the president of a western college shaved off his whiskers and threw them in the Mississippi. The fatal idea spread. President after president was tempted by it. Then at this very juncture the invention of the safety razor,—removing all danger to human life from the process of shaving,—brought a clean shave within the reach even of the most cautious. The president of the modern college and his senior professors are not to be distinguished from their first year students. Remove the whiskers and you remove the man. The whole stature and appearance of him shrink: his shoulders contract: his frame diminishes: his little bowler hat swallows and envelops his trivial skull.

The loss of scholarship is irreparable. Is it any wonder that Greek is dead, that Latin is dying and that the old time learning of the colleges gives place to a mere mechanical routine.

But most deplorable of all is the damage

that is being done to imaginative literature. Here, for example, are a few quotations selected, quite at random, from the great literature of the past to show the close interdependence of personality and whiskers:—

"The Duke remained seated in deep thought, passing his luxuriant beard slowly through his fingers."

(*Ouida.*)

Imagine what an impressive thing that must have been. The Duke could take his beard and let it trickle slowly through his fingers like rippling silk. No wonder that the Duke could *think,* when he could do that!

But all that can remain of that sort of passage in the books of today would run,

"The Duke remained seated in deep thought, passing his fingers aimlessly through the air a foot from his face, as if seeking, groping for something that he could not find."

Here again is a selection from the poet Gray's magnificent description of a Welsh bard.

"All loose his hoary hair, his beard
   Streamed like a meteor to the troubled wind."
                              (*Gray, The Bard.*)

The splendid picture,—the bard standing in the wind with the sparks flying from his whiskers in all directions,—is gone.

Or again, take Longfellow,—the opening lines of Evangeline.

"This is the forest primeval, the murmuring pines and the hemlocks
"Stand like Druids of old with beards that rest on their bosoms."

What a pity to have to change this to read:

"This is the forest primeval, the round smooth trunk of the gum tree
"Looks like a college professor divested entirely of whiskers."

In place of these noble pictures of the past we have nothing but the smooth-shaven hero of modern fiction, with his soopy-looking face, hardly to be distinguished from a girl's.   He may be seen on the cover of any of our monthly magazines. What can he do? He can *"press his clean-shaven face close, close to hers."* One admits, of course, that he has a certain advantage here. If he had whiskers he couldn't get nearly as close to her. But can he let his beard stream like a meteor to the wind with sparks of phosphorus flying off it in all directions? Can he "pass his beard through his hand?" No. Can he stand like a Druid of old? He can't.

As yet, happily, there are certain domains of our national life to which the prevailing degeneracy has not penetrated. The stage, the moving picture and the grand opera still hold their own. The stage villain still has his black beard. The Southern colonel still retains his mustachios. The scholar, the wise man and the magician of the moving picture keeps his black skull cap and his long white beard. The Wagnerian opera is as hirsute as ever. And those who have been privileged to see the pretty little operetta that Reginald de Koven left behind him, will have been pleased to note that Rip Van Winkle has a beard like an Ostermoor mattress reaching to his ears.

But can the stage stand alone? It can not. Something must be done. . . .

Fortunately for our civilization the best section of the public is already becoming alarmed. An effort is being made. A number of big, warm-hearted men, and a quantity of great big warm-blooded women are banding themselves together. This is a good sign. Whenever they do this,—and it is what they always do,— one feels that as soon as a sufficient number are all banded together something will be done.

As far as the United States is concerned to my mind there is only one possible remedy,— an amendment to the Constitution. Something, of course, might be done with magic lantern slides, or with moving pictures, or by taking up subscriptions. But these things demand money and time. Amending the Constitution does not. Experience is showing that it is a very, very simple thing, demanding only a little good will and forbearance as to which amendment gets through first. It is only fair that certain amendments now under discussion should have precedence. The proposal sent up from Kansas for amending the Constitution so as to improve the breed of steers in the West, and the Illinois amendment for shortening the distance between Chicago and the sea, are both admirable. But when these are carried an amendment in regard to the restoration of whiskers should be the earliest of our national cares. Individual freedom has its limits.

It is *not* true that a man's whiskers are his own. It is *not* true that he has the right to remove them. John Stuart Mill thought so. But Mill was wrong. Every individual is but a part of society; and if his station is such that a flowing white beard is demanded by it, his duty is obvious. No one would wish to carry too far the supremacy of the State. But a constitutional provision of a temperate character imposing compulsory white beards on college presidents, ministers, poets, ambassadors and grand opera singers would take rank at once as equal in common sense and

213

general utility with some of the most notable amendments to the Constitution of this Country.

THEN AND NOW

THE COLLEGE NEWS OF FORTY YEARS AGO AND THE COLLEGE NEWS OF TODAY

Medicals Take a Night Off

(As reported forty years ago)

Last night the students of the Medical Faculty took a night off and held their annual parade of the town. Forming up on the campus outside the windows of the dissecting room, the "Meds" moved in a compact body down College Avenue. Policeman McKonicky, who tried to stop them at the corner of Main Street, was knocked senseless and was deposited by two of the boys down the coal chute of the First National Bank. After upsetting a horse-car, the driver of which sustained certain injuries by inadvertently falling under the horse, the boys proceeded to the corner of Main and

The Restoration of Whiskers

First Streets where speeches were made exalting the progress of the Medical School, and where two more policemen were knocked senseless. The procession moved uptown again towards the president's residence carrying with it the front door of the First Baptist Church. After setting fire to the president's house the students adjourned to the campus where they started a bonfire in which, unfortunately, one or two bystanders were accidentally burned about the feet, hands, head and body. The arrival of a body of mounted police supported by a couple of squadrons of cavalry brought the evening to a close.

President Foible, on being interviewed this morning, stated that the damages to his house were quite insignificant, amounting to little more than the destruction of his furniture. The police who were unfortunately injured in their attempt to interfere with the students are reported as doing nicely. The driver of the street-car will be at work again in a week, and a cheerful tone pervades the whole college. The president further stated that the relations between the students and the town had never been better.

Medicals Take a Night Off

(As reported today)

Last night the students at the Medical Faculty took a night off from their arduous labours and were the guests of the Ladies' Reception Committee at the Y.W.C.A. building on Third Street. After the singing of a few of the better-known medical hymns and after being treated to a harmonium solo in B flat by the organist of the Insane Asylum, the students listened with evident enjoyment to a talk by the Rev. Mr. Week of the First Baptist Church on the subject "Where is Hell? Is it Here?" After the pastor had said everything that could be said on this interesting topic, each student was given a dish of ice cream and a doughnut. The president of the college in thanking the ladies of the Y.W.C.A. for their cordial reception said that he was sure the students would now return to their studies with renewed eagerness.

After singing "Rock me to Sleep, Mother," the gathering broke up at nine-thirty.

Philosophical Society Meets

(*As it used to forty years ago*)

Last night the Philosophical Society held the third of its bi-weekly beer parties in the supper room of the men's residence. After the reading of the minutes, coupled with the drinking of beer, followed by the usual routine of drinking the health of the outgoing officers of the week and the toast of welcome to the officers of the week following, the Chairman invited the members to fill their glasses and listen, if they cared to, to a paper by Mr. Easy on the Nicomachean Ethics of Aristotle. Mr. Easy, while expressing his regret that he had not had time to prepare a paper on the Nicomachean Ethics of Aristotle, delivered in place of it an excellent rendition of Bret Harte's "Heathen Chinee." At the close of the recitation the Chairman announced that the debate which had been an-

217

nounced on the topic *Are Mathematical Judgments Synthetically a Priori* had been abandoned owing to the fact that the topic involved more preparation than the members of the society were prepared to give to it. He suggested instead that the society, after filling its glasses, should invite Mr. Freak of the senior class to give his imitation of two cats quarreling on a roof. The invitation was followed by similar exercises and the meeting was sustained to a late hour, those of the members who went home leaving at about two a. m.

Philosophical Society Meets

(*As it does today*)

Last night a very pleasing meeting of the Philosophical Society was held in the parlour of the Women's Residence in the Martha Washington Building. Professor Strong in opening the meeting, said that she was glad to see among the members of the society a very creditable number of men, if she might use the phrase. She said no professor could feel that her work was satisfactory unless she could attract a certain number of men students. The professor then read her paper on the *Sociological Elimination of the Delinquent.* As the paper only lasted an hour and a half it was listened to in a luxury of enjoyment. The professor then having thrown the meeting open to questions, and a question having been asked, she very kindly spoke for another hour. At the close of the address a vote was taken on the resolution *That the Humbler Classes of Society Ought to be Chloroformed,* and was carried unanimously.

Discipline Committee Reports

(*As it reported forty years ago*)

The report is published this morning of the semi-annual meeting of the Discipline Committee of the Faculty of the College. This committee, consisting of the senior professors of the Faculty, was established, as readers will recall, about two years ago with the object of elevating the moral tone of the student body by expulsion, fines and the application of the criminal law. The Chairman reported that the committee had every reason to be gratified with the progress made during the period of its existence. The number of cases of suspension of students from lectures had increased under the operation of the committee by forty per cent; students warned, by sixty per cent; students found guilty of drunkenness, by seventy per cent; and students expelled for unbecoming and insubordinate conduct, ninety-five per cent. The report enumerates a new schedule of fines calculating to raise still higher the discipline of the institution, and recommends hereafter that every student guilty of striking or kicking a professor be brought before the committee and warned. The committee adds a further recommendation to the effect that measures be taken to let the student body understand that their presence at the University can only be tolerated within reasonable limits.

220

Student Control Committee Reports

(As it reports today)

The report is published this morning of the semi-annual meeting of the Students' Control Committee at the University. This Committee, as readers will recall, was established about two years ago with a view to raising the academic standard of the college. It is empowered not only to institute inquiries as to the capacity of the professors, but to recommend the expulsion of those of them who seem to the students' committee to be lacking in personality, or deficient in pep. The opening pages of the report deal with the case of the president of the college. A sub-committee, appointed from among the fourth year students in accountancy, have been sitting on the case of the president for six weeks. Their report is in the main favourable, and their decision is that he may stay. But the sub-committee pass severe strictures on his home life, and recommend that he has too many children for him to be able to give full attention to his college work, and suggests a change in the future.

The committee accepts and adopts the recommendation of the second year class in philosophy who report that the professor's lectures are over their heads, and ask for his dismissal. A similar request comes from the third year students in mathematics who report that the professor's lectures are below their standards.

The committee has received and laid upon the table the report of the fourth year class in commerce to the effect that they have thus far failed to understand any of the lectures that were ever given them, and ask that they be given their degrees and let go. The committee acknowledges in its report the gratifying statement made by the chairman of the Trustees in his annual report to the effect that student control marks another milestone on the arduous path that it is leading the college to its ultimate end.

VIII

LITTLE GLIMPSES OF THE FUTURE IN AMERICA

VIII.—Little Glimpses of the Future in America

I

The Final Solution of the Transportation Problem

(*An Extract from the New York daily press of 1930*)

RESUMPTION OF THE MAIL COACH SERVICE

WE are happy to announce to our readers that the mail coach service between New York City and Philadelphia, which has been temporarily suspended since 1840, is to be resumed this week. By a fortunate chance the well-known and highly popular coach, the Martin Van Buren, has been discovered still in her yard, where she was placed when she was set aside pending the experimental use of the railway, which has proved such a costly failure. Under the new arrangement,

225

passengers booked for Philadelphia are guaranteed of departure and arrival at the hour specified. Subject only to the hazards of the weather, the Martin Van Buren will leave her place of departure (The Andrew Jackson Hostelry, corner of Wall Street and the Albany Post Road) at or about daybreak on the morning of every Monday. This commodious coach has accommodation for ten inside and ten outside passengers. There is ample accommodation in the boot for all parcels and personal luggage. Passengers desirous of putting luggage in the boot, however, are requested to come to the booking office three days in advance to effect the necessary signature of vouchers, and to take the necessary oaths of allegiance and citizenship.

In order to avoid the present delays in the operation of the tunnel traffic, the Van Buren will be taken across the river on a barge. Passengers may keep their seats during the transit, or, for a small extra fee, may be carried across (if the wind serves) in a hoy. The Van Buren will proceed at full speed across New Jersey.

Absolutely no stops will be made except for the change of horses, for meals, and for the night.

When the moon serves, the Van Buren will continue her journey, still at full speed, until 9 P. M. She will arrive in Philadelphia, barring being struck by lightning, on the afternoon of the third day out of New York. The greatest satisfaction is expressed everywhere in business circles over the prospect of the speed and certainty offered by the new service. A peculiar and pathetic interest attaches to the fact that the four horses which drew the Van Buren on her last trip out of New York are all dead.

Other similar ones, however, have been secured from the hansom cab service of Fifth Avenue. Many of those who have seen the new team declare that it is hard to believe that they are not the original horses.

II

Form of Application to be Used in the Not-Very-Far Future in Trying to Secure a Hotel Room

(1) Letter from the Applicant.

227

The Management,
    The Soakus Hotel,
        New York.
Dear Sirs:

I beg to apply for a room, to be available for my use one month from the present date and usable for one day. I am a young man of good habits, a Presbyterian, a graduate of Harvard and a non-smoker. If you will see fit, Sirs, to trust me with a room I shall do my utmost to occupy it in a way entirely to your satisfaction. My testimonials are enclosed herewith.

                    Very faithfully,
                        EDWARD EATANYTHING

(2) Testimonial from the President of Harvard.

The Management,
    The Soakus Hotel,
        New York.
Dear Sirs:

This is to certify that Mr. Edward Eatanything attended the undergraduate course at Harvard for a number of years and obtained the Baccalaureate degree in Arts. His course included English Literature Courses 1, 2 and 6, Mathematics 4 and 5, and Latin 6 and 8. I consider him in every way fitted to occupy your room.

Very faithfully,

_____,

President, Harvard University.

(3) From the Pastor of the Broad Street Second Baptist Church.

The Management,
   The Soakus Hotel,
      New York.
Dear Sirs:

My young friend, Mr. Edward Eatanything, informs me that he is an applicant for a position as a roomer under your management. He was for over four years a member of my congregation and I have great pleasure in testifying that the level of his spiritual life is so high that you can with safety place him even on the top floor of your hotel.

Very faithfully,

——————————————,

Pastor.

(4) Certificate from the Metropolitan Emergency Guarantee and Insurance Company.

To Whom it May Concern:

Mr. E. Eatanything is insured in and by this company in compensation for all possible accidents resulting from rooming in a hotel. Any management permitting him to occupy a room is hereby assured that the Metropolitan Guarantee Company will see that he leaves the room, either alive or dead, at daybreak of the day following his occupancy.

(5) Answer from the Soakus Hotel Company.

Mr. Eatanything.

Dear Sir:

We have much pleasure in informing you that your application for a room has been accepted by the Board of Pardons of this hotel and ratified by the Conciliation Council of the Waiters' Union. The room will be ready for your occupancy at midnight of the day mentioned and you are requested to leave it at or before daybreak. An extra charge will be made for sleeping in the bed, or for the use of the window.

III

List of Honour, Pullman Company Announcement for March, 1930.

At a meeting of the Directorate of the Pullman Car Company, lower berths were awarded as follows for the month of March. The names mentioned below have been placed in order of merit. Here follow after the custom of the epoch the full honour roll of those to whom lower berths have been given.

IV

If the Immigration Laws Keep on Improving.

(*Extract from an article in a National Encyclopedia of 1975, entitled,—Deportation, Rise and Growth of*)

The practice of deportation first originated in the years of the Great War, during which the United States, aided by the Serbians, the Siamese, and other allies, conquered Germany. It was first applied to the Reds or Radicals. It proved an immediate success. The demand at once arose for the deportation of other classes of the community. The deportation of the Socialists and the Syndicalists was carried out in the years 1925-1930. The next deportation was that of the entire population of Paterson, New Jersey. A slight opposition was raised in the press at the time, but the improved appearance of the city of Paterson after the inhabitants were removed silenced complaint.

The decade following witnessed the deportation of the Osteopathists, the Chiropodists and the Homeopathists. The movement now assumed a racial or ethnographic character. In spite of furious opposition it was decided to deport the Irish and to insist on their living in Ireland. The claim of the Irish that they were law-abiding citizens threw the case into the Supreme Court where, after the dynamiting of three of the justices, the survivors held that the plea of the Irish was good. A similar claim raised by the Greek fruit sellers (*see under Peanuts*) was held void. The movement now assumed a distinctly religious character. The deportation of the Presbyterians may be said to have marked an epoch. All those who witnessed their departure from New York harbour, when a hundred pipers played *Lochaber No More* upon a hundred sets of bagpipes, felt that they never wanted to go through such an experience again (*see under Music, Definition of*). This deportation was followed by that of the Mayflower Society, the Sons and Daughters of the Revolution, the Mexican War Veterans, and other bodies whose existence had become a national danger. Of late years the deportation movement has undergone a marked decline.

The new sense of emptiness and space is inducing a feeling of loneliness throughout North America. Open regret is now expressed at certain of the deportations. It is widely felt that it was a mistake to send the Grand Opera Artists, the Choral Societies and other harmless bodies out of the country. It is expected that the present decade will witness a turn of the tide (*see under Tide*).

v

The Socialization of the Church

(A paragraph taken from any local paper in any Country Town in the year 1930)

The Vaudeville and Minstrel Show put on at the Fourth Street Church last night was in every sense a marked success. The occasion proved that the choice of the new pastor is indeed an admirable one. We have never, even at the Gaiety Theatre, seen better black-face work than that of the Rev. Mr. Hopgood last night, while his buck-and-wing dancing is better than that of any spiritual worker seen among us for

234

a decade. Several of the elders and church-wardens as end-men almost rivalled the honours of Mr. Hopgood. The dancing of the ladies of the congregation, who formed the chorus, particularly pleased us. Altogether we felt the Chairman was quite justified in his boast that the Modern Church has put the saloon out of business.

VI

If the "British Lecturer" Habit Grows

(*Items from a New York Daily of 1933*)

King George V lectured to a fair-sized audience at the Princess Theatre yesterday afternoon. The King's delivery is quite good and the comments on his personality are quite encouraging. Interviewed at the Biltmore today, King George expressed his surprise and pleasure at the size of America for which he prophesies a bright future.

Binghamton, N. Y., May 2. Mr. Lloyd

George and Mr. Georges Clemenceau have made a favorable impression here with their Readings from the Treaty of Versailles.

The British Ambassador has been accepted for the summer season work of the Orpheum Circuit. His platform work in his first appearance at Mauch Chunk, Pa., is pronounced decidedly good. His work will do much to create a better feeling between Singapore and Siam.

X

MY UNPOSTED CORRESPONDENCE

IX.—My Unposted Correspondence

IT is an old adage that second thoughts are best. This is especially true when second thoughts are fortified by the inertia of a lazy disposition, averse to trouble.

Like many other people, I find myself constantly impelled to write letters upon sudden impulse, or at least to frame them in my mind. But whether written or only "framed"—a much more agreeable process—somehow they never get posted.

These letters are addressed, for example, to the Directors of Theatres to tell them that their place is a fire-trap, and that I, for one, never propose to enter it again, and that, therefore, such poor profit as they are able to make must henceforth be made without me. But on second thoughts—after all, what if the place is a fire-trap, why bother? Let the other people burn. And, anyway, I rather think they are to have a musical revue there the week after next which I might like to see. Better chance it.

Another set of letters are framed to the Immigration Authorities in the United States, to tell them that I cannot consent to this everlasting questioning at the border. If the thing persists, I tell them frankly I must stop coming and going into their country. Indeed, I find that this is the general view of people, of both nations who come and go across the Canadian border. I have listened to conversations in the smoking end of the Pullman car which would make the President of the United States shake in his shoes. Once or twice I have almost written a strong letter. Nothing stopped me except the fear that they might take me at my word and keep me out.

But at other times the letters are not only "framed" but all written and signed, and only held back through the momentary difficulty of finding an envelope.

Witness this example:

Letter of Protest to the Light, Heat, and Power Company.

Sirs,

Your account for $41.85 just received this morning convinces me you are a pack of robbers. This bill which professes to represent an unpaid account for three month is incorrect. I paid you before. I know I did. The mere fact that I have got no receipt or anything of that sort is neither here nor there. I know I paid you because I have a distinct *feeling* that I have paid you.

This is a feeling which you ought to respect. My wife also remembers distinctly that she paid your collection man, or at any rate *a* collection man, at the door. And, anyway, look at the account itself. It is absolutely preposterous; six dollars for cooking-gas in one month! It can't be. We live plainly and, by Heaven, you couldn't use six dollars' worth of heat on all that we eat in a month if you tried. Then look at this charge for electric lighting. What is all this stuff about Kilo-watts? I never had any Kilowatts from you. And you have charged me apparently for thousands of them. My strong conviction is that that man of yours who reads the meter is a hired scoundrel.

In any case let me tell you this quite firmly. *I will not pay this bill*. If need be, I will go to prison for it for ten years. But I won't pay. Remember also that you cannot tyrannize over me as easily as you think. I have powerful friends. I know the cashier in one of our biggest banks, and a friend of mine knows the mayor quite intimately and calls him Charlie. You may find that if you lay a hand on me you are up against a body of public opinion that will shipwreck your company.

Yours savagely, ——

By the time this letter has been written and my wife has made a copy of it—so that when legal proceedings begin we can read it out to the whole court—it is dinner-time, and too late to bother to post the letter; in addition to which there don't seem to be any envelopes in the whole blessed house. After dinner I forget about it, and next morning when I see the letter lying on my table I begin to have doubts about the whole thing. After all, what's the good of a lot of fuss? The light company are scoundrels, but the way to deal with scoundrels is to be broad-minded. Furthermore, are they scoundrels? I'm not so sure on reflection that the collector was theirs, after all. I seem to remember that he was collecting for the home for the blind. And that big charge for the gas might be connected in a way with our having left the cooking stove burning all night once or twice by accident. And, after all, I have no receipts. Oh, pshaw! Let the thing go. The company, if they only knew it, have had a mighty narrow escape. After this I will keep receipts, check the meter myself, lie in wait for them, and then, when they least think of it, overwhelm with an action for criminal conspiracy. But meanwhile let it go. Here is the letter which I actually posted:

The Light, Heat, and Power Company.

Dear Sirs,

Enclosed, with apologies, my cheque for $41.85.

Very sincerely, ——

I suppose there are people in the company's office who open letters like that every month without realizing the wealth of invective that lies behind them.

Let me turn to a similar example:

Letter to the Head Office of the Railway Company in regard to the loss of my umbrella.

Here is a letter which speaks for itself. I have written it at least twenty times. So has everybody. But I have never yet posted it. Nevertheless, let the Railway Company be careful. The letter runs thus:

Dear Sirs,

I write to the Head Office of your Company because I have failed to get plain simple justice from any of your hired officials. Last week I left my umbrella in one of your Pullman cars. The name of the car, I regret to say, I cannot remember; but it was either Belgravia, or Ashdown, or some name of that sort. The names of all your cars, I may say, sound alike to me; and, anyway, you cannot expect me to remember them. Very good. I left my umbrella in this car. I want it back. It is not the value of the umbrella that I care about. What I really mean is that it's not the value of it, but the price of it. The thing concerned is matter of general principle; and when you hit me on a general principle you hit me where I live.

It will be not at all difficult for you to locate my umbrella, as it was left on the car between New York and Boston one day early last week. Up to the present time I have been unable to get any satisfaction whatever from your officials. I have been told that your district superintendent in New York is carrying an umbrella that is either mine or somebody's. May I add in conclusion that if I do not receive prompt satisfaction in this matter, I shall refer it to my solicitor?

I am yours, sir,

etc., etc. ——

Please note the very firm and decisive ending of this letter to the Railway Company. I am sure that, had it been sent, they would have been compelled to take action. It was only prevented being sent by my finding my umbrella under the hall table.

Another impulse from which often springs my unposted correspondence is an access of sudden philanthropy. Every time I hear that ten thousand Chinese have been drowned in a flood of the Hoang-Ho River I dash off a letter with a cheque in it for fifty dollars and the signature "Friend of China." But before it is posted I recall the fact that after all there are a terrible lot of Chinamen in the world —four billion, is it? Or is that the issue of German marks per day? Anyway there are so many that if they don't get drowned, what are they to do? Better wait for the next

246

flood, anyway. So the letter is never sent.

But second thoughts dull the edge of philanthropy every time. Indeed, sometimes the current of good deeds gets turned from its channel in the very process of giving. As witness this letter of a type that I am sure is quite familiar:

Sudden Access of Philanthropy after hearing
A Missionary Appeal.

The Reverend John Jungletalk.

Dear Sir,

Enclosed please find my cheque for a hundred dollars ($100.00)—one hundred dollars!

You do not know me, but I listened, sir, this morning to your sermon on behalf of the Tabloid Negroes of Tanganyika. I do not quite grasp where these negroes live, but your account of their condition has touched me to the quick. I am immensely moved by that story of yours about the old negro woman who wanted to hear a gramophone before she died or to die after hearing a gramophone (I

247

forget for the moment which). These people you told us of are in a deplorable condition. They are without Bibles, have no books, no soap, no hot water (I think you said hot water)—in fact they are in a bad way. And on the top of all this I gather that unscrupulous traders have come into the country and are selling rum and whisky to the natives for a few cents a bottle. This is terrible. In fact, sir, I find that as I write this letter I am inclined instead of sending you the hundred dollars to offer the higher sacrifice of personal service. I gather that you are to sail in a few weeks' time, going from here to San Francisco and there by steamer, to wherever it is that the Tabloid negroes live. I am more than half inclined to come along. If you can collect enough money for the two of us I will gladly do so. Meantime I will hold back the cheque of which I spoke.

Very sincerely in the spirit, ——

P. S.—That whisky you spoke of—is it Scotch or Irish?

I might have included above the letters which I (don't) write about the scorching of motors along my street—the other streets matter less—letters complaining that there are too many Flag Days, letters on Daylight Saving, Street Cleaning, Fly Killing, the League of Nations—in fact, it's endless.

X

LETTERS
TO THE NEW RULERS
OF THE WORLD

X.—*Letters to the New Rulers of the World*

No. I. *To the Secretary of the League of Nations.*

RESPECTED SIR,
     I have learned, as has everybody here in my home town, with unconcealed delight, of this new convention, that you have just concluded in regard to the Kalmuk Hinterland of the Oxus district. As we understand it here in our town, this convention will establish a distinct *modus vivendi* as between Monoglian Kalmuks and the Tartarian Honeysuckles. It will set up a new sphere of influence, the boundaries of which we are as yet unable to trace on the railway and steamship map of the world in our new Union Depot, but which we feel assured will extend at least fifty miles in either direction and will stop only when it has to. As citizens of a great country

253

it fills us with a new pride in this nation to reflect that the whole of this hinterland, both back and front, will now be thrown open to be proselytyzed, Christianized, and international-ized, penetrated and fumigated under the man-date of this country.

What you have done, sir, is a big thing, and when we realize that it has taken only six years for you to do it, we are filled with en-thusiasm as to what you are destined to do. Nor has this been the sole result of your years of labour. The citizens of our town have fol-lowed with a fascinated interest each stage of your achievements. Your handling of the claims of Formosa to a share in the control of the Ho-han Canal was masterly. On the news that you had succeeded in submitting to arbitration the claims of the Dutch bond-holders of the Peking-Hankow railway, our citizens turned out and held a torchlight pro-cession on the Main Street. When the word came that you had successfully arranged a *status quo* on the backwaters of the Upper Congo, there was an enthusiasm and excite-

254

ment upon our streets such as we have not seen since the silver election in 1896.

Under the circumstances, therefore, respected sir, I am certain that you will not mind a few words—I will not say of protest—but of friendly criticism. We readily admit in our town all that you have done for us. You have lifted us, as we fully recognize, into what is a larger atmosphere. When we look back to the narrow horizon of politics as they were in this town (you will recall our sending Alderman McGinnis and the Johnson boys to the penitentiary) we stand appalled. It is a splendid thing to think that our politics now turn upon the larger and bigger issues of the world, such as the Kalmuks, the Kolchuks and the internationalization of the Gulf of Kamchatka. It would have done you good, sir, could you have listened to the masterly debate at our Mechanics' Institute last week on the establishment of a six-nation control over the trolley line from Jerusalem and Jericho.

But, sir, to be very frank—there is a certain apprehension in our town that this thing is

255

being pushed just a little too far. We are willing to be as international as anybody. Our citizens can breathe as large an atmosphere as the Kalmuks or the Cambodians or any of them. But what begins to worry us is whether these other people are going to be international too. We feel somehow that your League ought, if we may use a metaphor, to play a little bit nearer home, not all the games but at least some of them. There are a lot of things in this town that we think might properly claim your attention. I don't know whether you are aware of the state of our sewers and the need for practically ripping up the Main Street and relaying them. Here is a thing in which we think the Kalmuks might care to help us out. Also if you would discuss with the Cambodians of the Sumatra Hinterland the question of their taking a hand in the irrigation of Murphy's flats (just the other side, you remember of where the old Murphy homestead was) it might make for good feeling all around.

Put very briefly, sir, our one criticism of

your achievements—and it is only said in the kindest possible way—is that your League is all right, but somehow the gate receipts of it seem to go in the wrong direction.

No. 11—To a Disconsolate King

My dear Charles Mary Augustus Felix Sigismund:

You will pardon me, I hope, this brief method of address. For the moment, I cannot recall the rest of your names.

I need hardly say how delighted and honoured I was to receive a letter from you written all in your own hand and spelt, as I saw at once, without help. It was perhaps wrong of you to pay insufficient postage on it. But I do not forget that you were once a king and cannot at once get over it. You write in what are evidently wretchedly low spirits. You say that you are living in Schlitzen-Bad-unter-Wein (if I get you right), in the simplest conceivable way. You have laid aside your royal title and are living incognito as the Hereditary Count in and of Salzensplitz. You have only a single valet and no retinue. You lunch, you tell me, very plainly each day upon a pint of Rheinwein and an egg, and at dinner you have merely a chop or a cutlet and a couple of quarts of Rudesberger. You retire to bed, it seems, after a plain supper—a forkful of macaroni, I think you said, with about half a tumbler of old Schnapps. Of all the thousands who fed at your table in the days of your kingship, none, you say, care now to share your simple fare. This is too bad. If they had you and your little table in New York, they could give you the choice of a line-up of friends that would reach from the Winter Garden to the Battery. But that is by the way.

The point is that you are singularly disconsolate. You tell me that at times you have thought of suicide. At other times you have almost made up your mind to work. Both of these things are bad, and I beg of you, my dear Sigismund, that before adopting either of these alternatives you will listen to a little quiet advice and will sit tight in Schlitzen-Bad-unter-Wein till things brighten up a bit. Unless I much mistake, my dear Charles Mary Felix, the world has not finished with you yet, nor won't have for a long time to come. It turns out, I am sorry to say, that the world is still an infinitely sillier place than we had imagined. You remember that morning when you ran away from your hereditary principality, concealed in a packing case and covered up with a load of hay. All the world roared with laughter at the ignominy and cowardice of your flight. You seemed all of a sudden changed into a comic figure. Your silly little dignity, the uniforms that you wore and that you changed twenty times a day, the medals which you bestowed upon yourself, the Insignia of the Duck's Feather which you yourself instituted—all these things became suddenly laughable. We thought that Europe had become sensible and rational, and was done with the absurdity of autocratic kings.

I tell you frankly, Charles Mary Felix, you and your silly baubles had been no sooner swept into the little heap, than a thousand new kinds of folly sprang up to replace you. The merry

259

Checkoslovak and the Unredeemed Italian ran up a bill of taxes for peaceful citizens like myself to pay. I have contributed my share to expeditions to Kieff, to Baku, and to Teheran and to Timbuctoo. General Choodenstitch is conducting huge operations against General Gorfinski in Esthonia, and I can't even remember which is my general and where Esthonia is. I have occupied Anatolia, and I don't want it. I have got an international gendarmerie in Albania that I think are a pack of bums, eating their heads off at my expense. As to Bulgaria, Bukovina, and Bessarabia, I believe I voice the sentiments of millions of free-born income-tax payers when I say, take them, Charles Felix; they are all yours.

The time is coming, I am certain, when a new pack of fools will come and hunt you up in your exile at Schlitzen-Bad-unter-Wein, clap a Field Marshal's uniform on you, put you in a bomb-proof motor car and rush you back to your hereditary palace. They will announce that you have performed prodigies of personal

260

bravery. You will wear again your twenty uniforms a day. You will give twenty-five cents to a blind beggar and be called the father of your people.

I give you notice, Mary Augustus, that when this happens, I shall not lift a finger to stop it. For it appears that our poor humanity, its head still singing with the cruel buffeting of the war, is incapable of moving forward, and can only stagger round in a circle.

No. III—To a Plumber

My very dear Sir,

It is now four hours since you have been sitting under the sink in my kitchen, smoking. You have turned off the water in the basement of my house and you have made the space under the sink dry and comfortable and you are sitting there. I understand that you are waiting for the return of your fellow plumber who has gone away to bring back a bigger wrench than the one that you have with you.

The moment is therefore opportune for me

261

to write these few lines which I shall presently place in an envelope and deliver to you on your departure.

I do not wish in any way to seem to reflect upon the apparent dilatoriness with which your work has been done. I am certain that is only apparent and not real. I pass over the fact that my house has now for two weeks been without an adequate water-supply. I do not resent it that you have spent each morning for a fortnight in my kitchen. I am not insensible, sir, to the charm of your presence there under the sink and I recognize the stimulus which it affords to the intellectual life of my cook. I am quite aware, sir, that all of these things are outside of the legitimate scope of complaint. For I understand that they are imposed upon you by your order. It is the command, I believe, of your local union that you must not use a wrench without sending for an assistant: it is an order of your federated brotherhood that you must not handle a screw-driver except in the presence of a carpenter and before witnesses: and it is the positive command of the international order to which you belong that you must not finish any job until it has been declared finishable by a majority vote of the qualified plumbers of your district. These things, no doubt, make for the gayety and variety of industry but interpose, I fear, a check upon the rapidity of your operations.

But what I have wanted to say to you, good sir, is this. You find yourself in possession of what used to be called in the middle ages a Mystery,—something which you can do and which other people can't. And you are working your mystery for all it is worth. Indeed I am inclined to think that you are working it for rather more than it is worth.

I think it only fair to tell you that a movement is now on foot which may jeopardize your existence. A number of our national universities have already opened departments of Plumbing which threaten to bring your mysterious knowledge within reach even of the most educated. Some of the brightest scientific minds of the country are applying themselves to find out just how you do it. I have myself already listened to a course of six speculative lectures on the theory of the kitchen tap, in which the lecturer was bold enough to say that the time is soon coming when it will be known, absolutely and positively, to the scientific world how to put on a washer. Already, sir, pamphlets are being freely circulated dealing with the origin and nature of the hot water furnace. It has been already discovered that the water moves to and fro in the pipes of the furnace with sufficient regularity and continuity of movement to render it capable of reduction to a scientific law. We shall know before long just what it is you do to the thing to stop it from sizzling.

You perceive then, my dear sir, that the moment is one which ought to give you room for anxious thought. You are perhaps not aware that a book has already been published under the ominous title *Every Man His Own Plumber*. It has been suppressed, very rightly, by the United States Government as tending to subvert society and reduce it to a pulp. But it at least foreshadows, sir, the grim possibilities of the future.

May I in conclusion make a personal request. If you have any friends who are in the bell-hanging business, or the electrical repair industry, or the broken window monopoly, or the loose-chair-leg combine, will you kindly show them this letter.

No. IV—To a Hotel Manager

Noble and Exalted Sir,

I am well aware as I stand before you at the desk of your rotunda, of what a worm I am. There is, as far as I can see it, no reasonable excuse for my existence. I have so it appears, "no reservation," and yet I have had the impertinence to come here and to sue for a room. The contempt with which you gaze upon me is only too well justified. It is of no use for me to plead that I did not know that I was coming and that my journey to your city was entirely unpremeditated. All this only indicates, as you justly express by the look upon your face, an ill-regulated life unfit for your consideration.

I am well aware, sir, that I ought to have written to you four months ago and entered myself upon your waiting list for accommodation: and I know that even in that case my chance of obtaining a room would have had to depend upon my continued merit of good conduct.

You inform me that if I lean up against this desk until one o'clock there is a possibility that a gentleman may vacate room 4601. This is glad news indeed. I shall stand here with pleasure and I am sure that you will not consider me disqualified if I stand first upon one leg and then upon the other. It is a habit that I have acquired in such hotels as yours.

Meantime, my dear sir, I should like, while I lean against the desk, to set down upon paper in a few words just what I think of you. I cannot help but contrast you, sir, with the old time "Proprietor" whom you have replaced.

The change, I do not doubt, is altogether salutary: and yet in certain aspects I cannot but regret it. The old-time "hotel man" was accustomed to meet me with an outstretched hand and a genial smile. He greeted me by my name and though I knew that he had read it on my valise my gratification was none the less. A room? Why, that man could find me a room if I turned up at midnight in the middle of a Grand Army Convention. A room! Why, the mere suggestion of my not getting a room filled him with distress. Sooner than see me sleepless he would put me in with two commercial men from the west (perfect gentlemen, as he himself informed me); he would put me, along with four others, on the billiard table; establish me behind a screen in a quiet corner of a corridor; or stop, rather, than see me suffer, he would offer (it was a safe thing) to turn out of his own room. As to a bath neither he nor I ever thought of it.

Observe that this man's hotel was very different from yours. In it was no palm room filled with rubber trees and resonant with the music of a Hungarian Orchestra: no Peacock corridor in which the Dangerous Debutante in the drooping hat shoots languorous glances at the passer-by. In point of pleasure and relaxation in his hotel there was nothing, other than the bar. That was the sole resort,—a quiet place below the stairs with a sanded floor and a long counter. And here it was that we stood in friendly converse, drinking whiskey and water while the chief clerk was "fixing me up" for a room. In those brave days we drank whiskey and water right after breakfast. We were supposed to need it.

Now, sir, I admit that you and your kind have made wonderful changes in our hotels. You have filled them with music and palm trees and debutantes. You have taught our people to drink English tea at five o'clock in the afternoon; you have borrowed the Café Chantant of the French and combined it with the grill room of the British. You have introduced afternoon dances and midnight suppers and you have gathered about you,—I admit it and I thank you for it,—all the prettiest women in New York to decorate your corridors.

You have become, and in a certain sense you are entitled to be, one of the New Rulers of the World. But this I ask. Do not push your sovereignty too far. If you do, there will be the inevitable reaction and revolution. A movement will be put on foot to build in your city a few hotels of the by-gone type of the old days when the guests were guests indeed and the kindly publican their host: a hotel with only one bath for every twenty-five guests: with dinner served only in the main dining room when the bell rings: without a single rubber tree in the whole extent of it,—but, and this is the essential point,—with something of the old fashioned courtesy and kindliness and quiet which you are banishing from your palatial doors.

What! The gentleman has vacated room 4601? Ah! a gentleman indeed! Quick, give me the pen and let me sign. I take back all that I have written. And by the way,

which is the way to the lunch room where the
Syrian dancing girls are? I shall want to eat
there.

No. V—To a Prohibitionist

My dear Sir:

Before I begin this letter let me explain that,
of course, I am myself a believer in prohibition.
I think that water, especially clear, cold water
—I don't care for muddy water—is a beautiful drink. I had a glass of it the other day,
and it seemed wonderfully limpid and trans-
parent—almost like gin.

Moreover, in the town in which I live, my
friends and I have seen prohibition in actual
operation, and we are all enthusiastic over it.
Crime is lessening every day. Murder is becoming almost unknown. Not a single one of
my friends was murdered all last summer. The
sale of boys' boots had increased a hundred per
cent. Some of the boys here have no less than
eight or ten pairs. Bank deposits are rising.
Credit is expanding, and work is almost ceasing.

These are very gratifying things, and when

we look back upon the old days, my friends and I wonder how we could have led the life that we did. I remember that very often in the middle of the morning we used deliberately to go out from our business and drink a glass of lager beer. Why we did this I cannot now conceive. Beer, sir, as you yourself are aware contains neither proteids nor albumen. It has less nitrogen in it than common starch, and is not nearly so rich in effervescent hydrogen as ordinary baking soda: in short, its food value is not to be compared with tan bark or with common mucilage. Nowadays, if I find that I flag at all in morning work, I take a little nip of baking soda and a couple of licks of mucilage and in a moment I am willing and anxious to work again.

I remember, too, that in the old times in the winter evenings we used to sit around the fire in one another's houses smoking and drinking hot toddy. No doubt you remember the awful stuff. We generally used to make ours with Bourbon whiskey and hot water, with just a dash of rum, with half a dozen lumps of white sugar in it, and with nutmeg powdered over the top. I think we used to put a curled slice of lemon peel into the rotten stuff and then served it in a tall tumbler with a long spoon in it. We used to sit and sup this beastly mixture all evening and carry on a perfectly aimless conversation with no selected subject of discussion, and with absolutely no attempt to improve our minds at all.

As things are now I have entirely cut all such idle acquaintanceship and such waste of time. I like to come home after my work and, after drinking four or five glasses of water, spend the evening with some good book of statistics, improving myself. I am then ready to converse, should an occasion arise, in such a way as to put conversation where it ought to be.

You will, therefore, readily understand that all my friends and I are enthusiastic over prohibition. If you were to ask us to go back to things as they were (but please do not do so), we should vote against it by a majority of easily two hundred per cent. It is on this account, with all the more confidence, that I am able to draw your attention to one or two points, in themselves very small things, in which we think that the present régime might be amended.

The first of these is the mere percentage, as it is commonly called, of the beer that is permitted to be sold. This is evidently a matter of very secondary concern and one on which no one would wish to dogmatize. But my friends and I feel that this percentage might profitably be placed at about, say, in rough numbers—twenty per cent. We should feel that at twenty per cent. we were getting a more adequate return upon the money expended. At the same time we lay no great stress on the particular figure itself. Twenty, thirty, or possibly still better, forty per cent. would prove quite acceptable to us.

Another point is the abolition of the bar. Here we are all agreed. The bar is done with forever. We never want to see it back. But we do feel that if we could have some quiet place where one could purchase beverages of the kind I have described, some plain room

273

with tables and a seat or two and possibly a
free lunch counter and a weighing machine,
we should feel better able to carry out the
general purport of the prohibition idea. There
are several of my friends who have not been
weighed since the first of July of 1919, and
are suffering grave inconvenience thereby.

I do not suggest that such a place should be
allowed to operate after the old unrestrained
fashion of the bars that kept open practically
all night. It should be placed under sharp regu-
lation. My friends and I feel that any such
place should be rigidly closed at two o'clock
A. M. with perhaps special facilities for access
at a later hour to the weighing machine and
the lunch counter. These, however, are mere
details of organization which, as we see it, do
not in the least impair the general principle.

As to whiskey and the stronger spirits, we
feel that there is not a single word to be said
for them. My friends and I are convinced
that the use of these things as a beverage is
deleterious to the last degree. We unite in
declaring that they should be regarded as medi-

cine and as medicine only. Two or three small incidents have occurred among us lately which have corroborated our opinion upon this point. Not very long ago one of my friends was taken, just outside of my door, with a very sharp pain, or stitch, in his side. For the moment I was at a loss what to do when it occurred to me that possibly a medicinal application of whiskey might prove effective. I took him into my house and administered it at once and was delighted to observe the color come back into his cheeks. It was some hours before I was enabled to remove him: but I finally ventured to put him into a hack, crosswise on the two seats, and the poor fellow was, I believe, safely placed against his own door by the hackman without further mishap.

Such incidents as this have convinced us that the sale of whiskey should be rigidly restricted to those who need it at the time when they need it, and in the quantity that they happen to need.

These suggestions, my dear sir, are intended merely as suggestions, as mere adumbrations of

275

possible modifications of the present system. We understand that there is some talk of reconsidering and redrafting the eighteenth amendment to the constitution. If this is so, I think it would be well to embody these suggestions in the new amendment. I am certain that upon these terms the Supreme Court of the United States would have no trouble with its interpretation.

No. VI—To a Spiritualist

Dear Friend and Brother in the Darkness,

I sent you last week a thought wave or movement of the ether. But it has apparently not reached you. I willed it in your direction and it seemed at the time to be moving toward you with gratifying rapidity. But I fear that it has gone clean past you. I am not however surprised or discouraged at this. In the little Spiritualistic circle to which I belong we have already learned to take the failures with the successes. We directed last week a thought wave at Senator Lodge but we have no reason to think that it hit him. The week before we had sent one, with special force, at Mr. Mackenzie King and there is no sign that it struck him. Our medium, Miss Mutt, tells us that very often a thought wave becomes supercharged and loses touch with the etherical vibrations and we all think this very likely. So I am not discouraged that my little message of congratulation and suggestion has gone astray. If I only had you near me I could get the message into you in a moment by putting the tips of my fingers on your cranium and willing it into you. But as I cannot do that I hope you will not mind if I have recourse to pen and ink.

What I want to say to you first of all is to congratulate you upon the splendid work that you have been doing in the world during the last few years. Until your recent activities began things were getting into a dreadful condition. Belief in everything seemed to be dying out. All idea of a material hell had had to be abandoned and there seemed nothing left. But now all that has been completely changed and I am sure that the little circle to which I belong is only one among thousands that are bringing hope and light to a world that was growing dark.

I am sure that you will be glad to learn that in our little circle our experiments have been singularly successful. We began in the very simplest way because Miss Mutt, our medium, said that it was better to begin with simple things so as to find out whether our members offered an easy mark to the ether waves sent from the Other Side, and they did. As our first experiment we all sat around a table with our fingers just barely touching it. We all had our eyes bandaged except Miss Mutt and we put the light out in the room to avoid the cross vibrations.

We were all delighted to find that the table at once began lifting its legs in the air and making raps on the floor and presently it ran right around the room and then climbed up the wall. Miss Mutt had to coax it down again. This of course is only a very simple thing and Miss Mutt, our medium, explained it all very clearly by telling us that the table had moved out of the subliminal plane and had got into

278

a plane of its own. But at first it seemed quite surprising.

After that we went on to quite a lot of other experiments and sent telepathic messages clear out into space beyond the stars, and produced actual bodies and raised the dead and things like that. These are only little things, of course, and to you I am sure they sound nothing. But I can't tell you how these simple little experiments pleased and delighted us.

Our séances in our little circle have now taken a more or less regular form. We meet on Tuesday evenings at 8 and first we have coffee and then Miss Mutt goes into a trance and calls up for us the spirits of any of the great people in history. The members generally vote as to who is to be called up but if there is any dispute the hostess of the evening decides what spirit is to come. We have had Machiavelli and Queen Elizabeth and a Roman Emperor who was awfully good though I forget his name for the minute. Machiavelli gave us a most interesting talk on the tariff and made it as clear as anything. He said that where he is they understand all about it. At nine o'clock Miss Mutt comes out of the trance and we have cake and ice cream and arrange where the next meeting is to be.

So I need hardly tell you that in our little circle we appreciate very much indeed the sort of work that you and other leaders are doing. Miss Mutt our medium says that it will be splendid when you yourself are on the Other Side. We shall send a wave at you right away.

I am sure then that you will not take amiss the very few words of criticism that I feel inclined to add to my letter. Perhaps I should not exactly call it criticism so much as suggestion as to how things might be made better still. As things are now we have all felt a certain amount of disappointment at what seems to be the low mental standard of the spirits that talk to us. Machiavelli for instance seemed to get all mixed up about what *ad valorem* duties meant and when McSmiley, one of our members who is in the wool trade, asked him about schedule K, he seemed to get quite angry and he said that where he was there was no schedule K. Miss Mutt, our medium, reminded us afterward that Machiavelli had died of softening of the brain so I suppose that accounts for it. But I never knew that George Washington's brain had softened too before he died and that poor Longfellow had had it very badly,—indeed apparently for years.

I think Sir that it will help along séances like ours immensely if you could manage to do something to keep up the education of the spirits. Miss Mutt says that they have books on the other side just as we do here. But one wonders if they read them. I suppose that in a sense they must get fearfully restless rushing round in the void, and it must be hard for them to sit down quietly and pick up a book. But I do believe that if they could be persuaded to do so, it would be a splendid thing for them. Perhaps too they could be taught to play bridge, or to knit. But I think that something really ought to be done to brighten up their minds a little. McSmiley left our little group after the Machiavelli evening because he said the spirits were just a pack of dubs. We all felt that this was wrong but we decided at once to send out a thought wave at you and ask about it. I am so sorry that nothing seems to have hit you.

THE END